Earth Rising II

The Betrayal of Science, Society and the Soul

By Dr. Nick Begich & James Roderick

Earthpulse Press Incorporated
P. O. Box 201393
Anchorage, Alaska 99520

www.earthpulse.com

ISBN: 1-890693-44-8

Cover Art Design: Nick Begich & Shelah Slade
Images by NASA and the US Park Service

First Printing
First Edition

Printed in the United States of America

Biography

Dr. Nick Begich is the eldest son of the late United States Congressman from Alaska, Nick Begich Sr., and political activist Pegge Begich. He is well known in Alaska for his own political activities and internationally as a futurist and lecturer, having presented throughout the United States and in nineteen countries. Twice elected President of the Alaska Federation of Teachers and the Anchorage Council of Education, he has been pursuing independent research in the sciences and politics for most of his adult life. Begich received his doctorate in traditional medicine from The Open International University for Complementary Medicines in November 1994. He co-authored the book *Angels Don't Play This HAARP; Advances in Tesla Technology* with Jeane Manning, and *Earth Rising – The Revolution: Toward a Thousand Years of Peace* co-authored with James Roderick in January 2000. He is also the editor of Earthpulse Flashpoints and has published articles in the areas of science, politics and education. He has been featured as a guest on thousands of radio broadcasts reporting on his research activities including new technologies, health and earth science related issues. He has also appeared on dozens of television documentaries and other programs throughout the world including BBC-TV, CBC-TV, TeleMundo, and others. Begich has served as an expert witness and speaker before the European Parliament. He has spoken on various issues for groups representing citizen concerns, elected officials, scientists and others. He is the publisher and co-owner of Earthpulse Press and works under contract for the Chickaloon Village Council, a federally recognized American Indian Tribe of the Athabascan Indian Nation. Dr. Begich is married to Shelah Begich-Slade and has five children. He resides just north of Anchorage in the community of Eagle River, Alaska, USA.

James Roderick was a 30-year resident of Alaska, working variously as a fisherman, gold-miner and trapper. His investigations into military toxins in Alaska led to stories in the press about chemical weapons disposal in Alaska's waters, nuclear power plant contamination in central Alaska and the military's illegal testing of Alaska natives and Eskimos with radioactive Iodine. Cofounder of the No HAARP efforts in 1991. Joined Earthpulse Press as a research associate in 1993 providing some of the most insightful research in technology areas and background research for lectures and public events. Coordinated the media relations and customer relations for Earthpulse Press from September 1998 - August 2002. *Co-author of Earth Rising – The Revolution: Toward a Thousand Years of Peace* in 1999. Contributing author and editor of the Earthpulse Flashpoints as well as articles written for publication in dozens of publications around the world. James co-authored this book through his drafting of sections, research and editing up until the last weeks of his life in August 2002.

CONTENTS

Dedication

As writer's, Jim and I often talked about how it was that we were given the great gift of being able to research and disclose the issues in the following pages. We both believed strongly that we had answered our calling in this part of our life – to speak the words that needed to be heard. Together, I think, we do this well in these pages. We also both understood we could not do it alone and that behind us was the support of our families and close friends. Many people over the years have had the belief that Earthpulse Press Incorporated was a large organization with many employees and people to assist, while the reality is, the day-to-day work was done by just two of us. There are a number of people who contributed to our efforts that are referenced in the writing and in the footnotes of this book. Their efforts have been outstanding because the material would have been left wanting without their individual contributions. To each of them we thank you.

Behind the organization are the people that allow us to do our work. What many are unaware of is the sacrifice of others so that things can move forward as they have over the years. My wife, Shelah Slade, has been a stable force behind us supporting James and I while enduring long absences and my seventy-eighty hour weekly work schedules. At the same time, she has been meeting the many challenges of maintaining a household of three children and being active in community affairs. This work moves because she cares in a wonderfully loving way.

I have also been fortunate to have been blessed with wonderful in-laws who are a few blocks away. Glen and Betty Slade have spent a number of early days and late nights getting me to and from airports, helping with children, and just being there when we needed the help the most. The last several years have presented great challenges to James and I as we struggled to finish this book and keep everything else moving. Betty and Glen were always there to help, run someone somewhere or cook a meal when everyone else was too exhausted and for this I am eternally thankful.

Jim died before these last words were written. His mother, who passed away in the summer of 2002, was an inspiration to him and, in their weekly calls, a source of compassion and endless support. Carolyn and Paul Roderick, Jim's brother and sister-in-law, had helped him through the roughest times and were there as family always is – supporting each other. His efforts were enriched by the love of family, friends and those who cared enough to do something good in the pursuit of otherwise busy lives.

I thank my adopted Athabascan families for their support while attempting to finish this book, help the Village of Chickaloon and meet my other obligations in life. My Athabascan family has given me the benefit of an experience in compassion where I have learned much that will resonate with my writing for the remainder of my life. The wisdom of our clan Grandmother Katherine Wade, Chief Marie Smith-Jones, Chief Gary Harrison and others I have met in my work have reminded me of the roots of our struggles, as human beings, and the force of love in overcoming all obstacles.

It is through all of these people that any of this has been accomplished. These are the living angels who never have their trumpets blown until the Creator says, "well done my good and faithful servant." To all of you we thank you.

Prologue

We have always tried to do more than just research the stories and issues that we report on – we have immersed ourselves in the process as activists do – blending real and sustained actions with our words. This is how things happen – by taking what is in the center of our soul, what we know to be right and true, and converting into direct action. Even in the midst of adversity the work continues.

My co-author, best friend, and fellow activist James Roderick passed away from natural causes on August 10, 2002 as this book's research was nearing completion. I cannot explain how much Jim meant to me and my family with only words. He was like my brother. I used to tell people if they called my office they would get either me, my wife Shelah or Jim and that whoever they got it would be like talking to me. Most people do not even know how much Jim did to get these issues out to the public the last few years.

James Roderick lived a simple life with little regard for physical things. His eye was toward making the world a better place. On a foundation of nothing physical in terms of economics Jim believed that a single person, even with nothing in his pocket could still reach out with what he had and do something truly great for someone else. He did not seek either recognition or reward. He only sought to do, to take an action that might further what he believed was right and true. He knew "trying" was what was required. Not winning or losing by the world's standards but always trying no matter what the obstacles. Jim knew that the spirit of a single soul contained more power than a thousand suns. He knew that his connection to the universe and the Creator would allow him the opportunity to serve a greater good, and he was committed to do so, and he did. Jim lived below the poverty level his entire life, had none of the material advantages of even the average person in this country. Yet he knew what he did have, and he gave that until his last breath escaped him, and his soul departed while surrounded by his best friends and closest family members.

An environmental activist credited with organizing the food supply for sea otters during the infamous Alaska oil spill in Prince William Sound, Jim engaged in what he believed in. He was responsible for helping break several of the major environmental news stories in this part of the world – only a few of us even knew him as one of the key sources.

After spending several years caring for his father before he died, Jim Roderick began to follow the strange tale of HAARP. Jim, an activist fighting military toxins at the time, had tripped over the HAARP story in 1991. He had a great sense for these things and knew he smelled a rat. He joined with two others and formed NO HAARP two years before I was involved in these issues. When I met Jim in 1993, he and his friends had exhausted their resources and energy and were discussing giving up the fight. It was just before that time that I published my first article on HAARP triggering a chain of events, which culminated in the book *Angels Don't Play This HAARP* (with co-author Jeane Manning). Half of the references in that work were compiled by the original NO HAARP'ers and safeguarded by Jim Roderick. After consultation with his colleagues they agreed to transfer the archives to me and we agreed to continue to fight the fight together. As the years rolled on and the book was published, Jim, my wife and I stayed the course of NO HAARP for what has now been 8 years. We raised and spent $2 million dollars in opposition to HAARP through the sale and promotion of our intellectual property – what was in our heads and hearts.

We wrote together to change the world and did with the research and publication of our first book together, *Earth Rising – The Revolution*. Every achievement I have made in these years, as a person, could not have been accomplished without Jim Roderick and my wife Shelah. When you see and hear me in the future I hope you also all remember Jim and my wife, who remains beside me in each day's battles. On August 9, 2002, the day before Jim died, I was able to let him know that the debate on HAARP had reached a new level with the Russian Duma (their national legislature) passing an action in opposition to HAARP.

Four years ago, after we had worked together at a distance, Jim had a brush with death. At that time we were told that Jim had a week to live. My wife and I rushed to the airport to fly to

Homer, Alaska to see our ailing friend. Then the miracle happened. His liver functions returned and his body began to heal. He was released a few days later. We decided we needed Jim closer to us and he would gain a greatly improved working environment. We arranged for the big move to Eagle River and had him relocated a few blocks from my family. A few months later began a series of events that would make his last four years his best at a time when I was going through my worst. Together Jim held my right side up and my wife held my left. Without their support nothing would have been accomplished the last four years. These are the unsung heroes who no one ever sees. It was during this time that Jim and I co-authored our first book and began working on the book you are now reading.

Shortly after Jim arrived in Eagle River, one of our closest friends and activist Gael Flanagan died. Gael was not only our good friend she was one of my mentors, like my wife's sister and like a second mother to my children. She was also the wife of Patrick Flanagan who's biography, *Towards a New Alchemy,* I authored in 1998. Patrick was once counted among my closest friends. He is no longer my friend.

Gael died through the ingestion of "several hundred times" the lethal dosage of the drug ketamine according to the medical examiner. There are many unanswered questions surrounding her death. The medical examiner's report ruled out suicide but left open the question of accident or murder?

After Gael died, Patrick intensified a year-old pattern of increasingly bizarre behaviors that caused a series of events that began to crush our ability to continue as an organization. Earthpulse was in trouble. I asked Jim if he wanted to stay or go back to Homer because I knew it was going to be a hard fought battle to maintain the company and deal with Patrick. Jim refused to leave – he was in it until the end. My work was also Jim's work.

In the midst of our research and writing over the last four years a great deal has happened. I took additional work responsibilities to pay the bills and try and keep Earthpulse going while Jim held down the fort and kept the day-to-day work of Earthpulse moving. My fight with Flanagan smoldered and then was turned into litigation when I sued him and his companies. The impact of the violations against me by Flanagan led to my personal bankruptcy in 2002. In the two weeks before Jim died we began intense negotiations to settle the litigation with Flanagan and were offered a settlement valued at about $100,000 – a small part of what we had lost from the effects of our "Flanagan experience". The settlement would have required our silence on any issues concerning Patrick, Gael or his affiliated organizations.

The cash would have gone far in rebuilding Earthpulse Press in its capacity to continue the work we began in 1993, but it could not be accepted on the terms of silence. We rejected the settlement and withdrew from the process closing our opportunity to continue the litigation against his organizations. The truth does not have a price – to agree to silence is the essence of *The Betrayal of Science, Society and the Soul,* the subtitle to this book. By October, 2002 we were discharged out of bankruptcy and given the opportunity to continue our work on the issues contained in these pages.

Many have helped us in the last several months which has made this book's publication possible. We are building a new organization and will continue to publish our reports and books. We do not know what the future holds or all the details, but I am committed to complete what we have begun. I am committed to fighting the good fight on all fronts. What Jim has reminded me of so strongly in his passing is that nothing can suppress the soul and spirit of a person. This is the central message in this exposé which was researched, written and published while facing challenges in every area.

This book was written over a three year period fraught with adversity, delays and personal challenges. It seemed every obstacle would rise before us and be met by sheer persistence and will power. While being supported by many people who continue to contribute to our work, this book is finally complete.

Life delivers adversity and opportunity. It is we who choose how to use the life we have. In the end of life, we hope we hear the words from Creator, "Well done my good and faithful servant" – words, I am sure, my co-author James Roderick has already heard.

In the future remember Jim and recognize in ourselves our own individual potentials as human beings. Do something good for someone on the planet in memory of what the many unsung heroes have done for each of us. May Creator Guide Our Footsteps.

Dr. Nick Begich
March 11, 2003

Chapter 1

A Call to Service

This book was researched with the dedicated support of many friends of Earthpulse Press but most particularly my co-author James Roderick who worked with me on this project until his death. I have struggled with the book in many ways in attempting to bring it forward as a testament to my dear friend, colleague and fellow traveler. This book had been planned for release for over two years and was delayed by a number of obstacles but, at last, it is in print.

There are four primary issues discussed in this book. There is a chapter about new underwater sonars being planned by the United States military even while they acknowledge the risks to life in the seas. In the second section, cell phones and their risks to people are considered as we head into a new wireless world. The third section deals with information systems and related technologies. The last section includes a discussion of the erosion of personal privacy in the United States and around the world based on new technology. When not developed on a platform of civility and truth these new technologies betray the essence of science as servant, and not master, of the creative human soul and the life systems of the planet.

Earth Rising II: The Betrayal of Science, Society and the Soul is a book that looks at data in order to show a trend or direction which needs careful review. The book makes use of over three hundred direct quotes from public records and news reports, coupled with the experiences of the authors. In the end we put forward solutions and ideas for change. It is the hope of the authors that this book is transforming. It is hoped that these words ignite a spark of the fire of the Creator which we believe resides in all of us as a force to encourage us to be activists for truth.

As in our last book, we need to point out a few important ideas about why it is imperative that we begin to awaken to both our potentials as humans and our obligations as stewards. People have created and developed technology since the discovery of ways to make fire and the invention of the wheel. Technology advanced slowly for perhaps millions of years according to our knowledge of history, speeding up as calculating technologies and other human intellectual abilities emerged. By the end of the 20th century the pace of change had moved to transition speeds where human knowledge was doubling every ten months. At this pace it has become difficult for most of us to keep up, much less consider either short-term or long-term impacts of these quickly advancing technologies. We, at Earthpulse Press, cull material from thousands of documents in order to attempt to bring together the mosaic which forms the reality of the impact of these new sciences.

I have often been asked what motivates the work I do and why I engage in these efforts when clearly other paths could have been followed. I come from a political background in a home where there were exciting and spirited debates of public policy, principles of democracy within a republic and the ideals of human justice, liberty and freedom. Public debate in civil society was the hallmark of my upbringing which required a sense of fair play, openness and most importantly honest expressions of the truth. At fourteen years old I lost my father in an airplane disappearance while he served in the 92nd United States Congress as the lone Congressman in the House of Representatives from Alaska. When he was lost with the House Majority Leader, Hale Boggs, it was a few weeks before the second election of Richard Nixon as President and the revelations which sprung from the Watergate Scandal in the early 1970s. It was twenty years later when information emerged that indicated perhaps this disappearance was more than an accident.

It's ironic to think that Hale Boggs and my father were fighting many of the same issues we have taken on today. The issues of education, Native American rights, military issues, government accountability and personal privacy have all been central to our work the last eighteen years.

The Disappearance

"Because he had no race of his own to fight, Hale [Boggs] was speaking on behalf of colleagues all over the country, as was I. From mid October, when Congress was expected to adjourn, until Election Day three weeks later, we had accepted fifteen speaking engagements between us. Hale went down to Texas for a speech, and President Clinton later told me of the next day, when he, as a young Democrat from Arkansas volunteering in the Texas campaign, drove Hale to the airport for his flight back to Washington."[1] where he caught his plane connections to Alaska to campaign for Nick Begich. "Nick Begich was a vibrant, outspoken Democrat – a 40-year-old father of six running for his second two-year term. He had asked Boggs to come to Alaska to campaign for him, even though the Republicans had mounted only token opposition.

The opposition was Don Young, a state senator from Fort Yukon. Young's campaign was poorly financed, partly because Begich was regarded as a sure thing.

And he was. Three weeks after his plane disappeared, the congressman who was presumed dead defeated Young with 55 percent of the vote."[2] My father was a popular political leader in Alaska and the search which ensued proved to be the most intense in the history of the United States and yet did not find a trace of the airplane in the official search record.

"The day after an airplane carrying House Majority Leader Hale Boggs (D-La) and Rep. Nick Begich (D-Alaska) vanished in Alaska 20 years ago, the US Coast Guard received a mysterious report that a radio call from the downed plane had been picked up and that two of the plane's four passengers were still alive.

"The story in the report, which has never before been revealed, is contained in FBI documents obtained last week by *Roll Call* under a Freedom of Information Act request."[3] That request and article was the first official indication of the very foul

1 Boggs, Lindy and Hatch, Katherine. *Washington Through A Purple Veil: Memoirs Of A Southern Woman.* Copyright 1994. Published by Harcourt Brace & Company. EPI3405

2 Enge, Marilee. "Begich mystery endures." Oct. 16, 1992. *Anchorage Daily News* EPI3554

3 Simpson, Glenn R. "Report on Hale Bogg's Downed Plane Disclosed." Aug. 3, 1992. *Roll Call* EPI3555

play and/or incompetence that had been the real cause behind the event. The fact that Boggs had criticized the FBI and J. Edgar Hoover, calling for his resignation some months before, the fateful flight in Alaska. Even though Hoover was gone by the time of the flight the FBI was in need of an overhaul. Boggs was a reformer who was in a position to change the FBI into an agency which was accountable to the congress and the Constitution. At the time the FBI had been tapping congressional phones, infiltrating protest groups and interfering with basic free speech and assembly rights of Americans.

Boggs, as Majority Leader in the United States House of Representatives, was one of the most powerful democrats in the congress at a time when corruption was being exposed through the release of the Pentagon Papers, the Watergate scandal and other major stories were being told. Boggs was angry at the FBI's abuses of power particularly the tapping of congressional phone lines, student groups and other highly questionable activities. As a member of the Warren Commission (the assassination investigative body after the death of John F. Kennedy), he wanted the investigation reopened. Boggs was an outspoken advocate for civil rights and open government, a platform not shared by Nixon or his administration as they trampled the Constitution and the values of the American people, using the government as if it were a private club.

Although the FBI records were credible the government decided it was not worth following up twenty years later. "State officials decided not to reopen the search for the Cessna 310 carrying then US House Majority Leader Hale Boggs of Louisiana and US Rep. Nick Begich because the area suggested by the tipster has since been searched many times over the years for other crashes, and not a scrap of the plane's wreckage has been found." 4 What was not considered was that the plane could have been covered in ice and snow. The location was the center of an ice field in southeast Alaska. Modern ground penetrating sensors of various kinds could easily have revealed the location if a metal airplane was there. The area where the plane was reported is regularly used for military exercises which could, as a part of their training, locate the crash site. The very technologies we

4 Randall, Gail. "No new search for Begich." Aug. 8, 1992. *Anchorage Daily News* EPI3560

expose in our writing are those that the military could have used while engaging in their regular exercises in the area – perhaps someday they will.

The Mystery

The story below was authored by my brother Tom in revealing the history of the disappearance. I am often asked about the details. It seems that the mystery surrounding these events leads to the same root problems of government demonstrated by the Nixon administration where betrayal of the public trust was exemplified in all its ruthlessness.

"The following events are drawn directly from interviews and newspaper accounts of the events following the downing of the Cessna 310 carrying Congressmen Nick Begich and Hale Boggs, Begich aide Russ Brown, and pilot Don Jonz.

Juneau, Alaska is known for its rain and fog. The morning of October 16th, 1972 was no different. The drizzle was steady, the clouds low, the airport backed up. Bob Cooksey glanced at his watch as the schedule ran through his mind. The cocktail party, the fundraising dinner that evening. It all had to be kept on schedule – not an easy thing to do when the plane was already fifteen minutes late. But, with the patience borne of experience, Cooksey settled down to wait. Planes were often delayed on the Anchorage to Juneau run. Fifteen more minutes went by. Cooksey went to the flight tower just to be sure that the plane had left Anchorage. No problem, he was told, the plane had left a little late. A weather delay. Just hold on, they will be here. Why not have a cup of coffee? Have a seat? After an hour Cooksey knew that something had gone wrong.

> 'BOGGS, BEGICH PLANE MISSING' by Paul Anderson Anchorage, Alaska *(UPI)* 'A fleet of thirty planes was thrown into a massive search today for a light plane lost over the Alaskan wilderness Monday...'

Sunday night Nick Begich leaned over to Margaret Pojhola in the ballroom of the Westward Hotel as a crowd of well-wishers pressed him with their hands and words. The success of the evening filled him as he managed a 'Don't leave...' before the crowd overwhelmed him. After a few moments the number of people around the Congressman had grown no smaller. It was time for Margaret to take action. Using an old campaign ploy, she spoke to him while pushing through the crowd, her voice loud so that all those around would not miss a word. 'Nick, if you don't leave now you're going to miss your next appointment!'

Deferring to Margaret, Nick nodded his thanks to his supporters and walked out of the hotel into the wet Anchorage night. Margaret's husband Carl brought up the car and they drove to the nearby Travelodge. There they met two other friends, Bill Sheffield and Wendall Kay, both old-time Alaskan politicos. October was a time of year heavy with politics and the future was looking bright for Alaska's Democrats. The five sat down to talk. Bill was picking up the tab.

After an hour Sheffield and Kay moved on, carrying the politics with them. Nick relaxed. Though the hour was late, he asked Carl and Margaret to stay. He wanted to talk about other things, personal things. This was one of those rare moments when politics did not pace him. They stayed and talked. The glow of the evening had not yet left him. He talked about the night, of the mood of the crowd. His eyes reflected the wit of the laughter-filled words of Louisiana Congressman Hale Boggs, who had flown up to show his support for the first term Democrat from Alaska. He talked about his family, and seeing his wife Pegge the day before in St. Cloud, Minnesota in the middle of another of the seemingly endless trips back and forth from Washington D.C. to Alaska. He joked about his home, his kids, and the future. He was in a state of euphoria, on top of the world. In his words he wrapped them in his life as only friends can.

But the evening had to end. There was a full schedule in Juneau the next day starting early in the morning. He saw them off at their car. 'I'll be back in town next Saturday' he said. 'I'll call you then.' The Pojholas drove off as Nick stepped back into the hotel.

There are times when a feeling comes over you, a foreboding, a doubt, the origins of which you can't quite place. Though the evening had been one of the most enjoyable in memory, Margaret felt that foreboding now. As they drove the feeling grew until, sick with an overwhelming fear, she turned to Carl and spoke the first words uttered since they had left Nick in the rain-drenched parking lot of the Travelodge. 'Something terrible is going to happen' she said.

> SEARCH EFFORTS CONTINUE FOR MISSING PLANE BEGICH, BOGGS ABOARD; PLANE PRESUMED DOWN' by the *Empire* Staff and the *Associated Press*'...in Juneau, Coast Guard aircraft began search operations early this afternoon after waiting all morning for fog to lift.'No aircraft had arrived or departed Juneau airport this morning because of the foggy conditions...'

In Juneau Alaska Education Association (AEA) lobbyist Bob Van Houte tried all day to pick up a distress signal from the lost plane on his 'ham' radio. Political ally and friend of Nick's, he refused to believe that the plane was not out there somewhere waiting for the weather to clear, waiting for the rescue craft to find them. But there was nothing. There had been an emergency locator beacon on the plane, but it did not seem to have been activated. Or, if it had, it was where no radio could pick up its transmission. He tried again the next day, and then the next.

Gene Kennedy, Nick's Administrative Assistant and best friend, flew in to Juneau from Anchorage and chartered a helicopter to search for the missing plane. They searched all day up and down the inlets and passages around Juneau, Douglas and the surrounding islands. No trace of the plane could be found.

On Monday Kennedy had given his seat on the ill-fated flight to Russ Brown, Nick's aide. Brown had been unable to afford the commercial flight to Juneau and had asked Kennedy to switch places with him. Gene had agreed.

He couldn't believe that a life as vibrant as his friend's might be over. There was no way it could have happened so quickly, Nick was too young. The days passed but still he waited for word.

As the hours passed Harry Lupro's hopes dimmed. Co-chairman of Nick's campaign in Juneau, he had to go to the events regardless of whether the candidate was there. He headed to the scheduled dinner that night. At least he could tell those who might not have heard what had happened. When he arrived at the Baranof Hotel he found that the few people milling about already knew.

> 'RAIN, FOG SLOW SEARCH' by Howard Weaver *Daily News* Staff Writer 'An armada of aircraft was all but idled Wednesday, as weather conditions along Alaska's coast continued to thwart searchers looking for the plane, which carried Rep. Nick Begich, House Majority Leader Hale Boggs, and two other men on a flight from Anchorage to Juneau....'

'The Rookies' was on television keeping the kids under control as they sprawled on the couch and floor in rapt attention. When the phone rang moments later, the children looked at each other, hesitating before one of the boys hopped up and ran into the den to answer it. He returned seconds later and climbed back into his perch on the couch.

'It's for you Ma, some Governor or something....' he said and then the sirens of the T.V. show had absorbed him.

A Governor? Pegge thought. It could only be Bill Egan. But why would he be calling? When she picked up the phone she found it was 'Governor Bill'. He spoke quickly and to the point. His was the first call to tell her that her husband's plane was missing. She listened quietly and asked for a progress report. He brought her up to date. When he was done she thanked him and hung up the phone. Calmly she returned to the children, sat down in front of the television and stared at the screen. The children barely noticed her return, absorbed by the action of the show. Though she watched with them, she did not see the images.

The first thing that Lindy Boggs saw when she stepped out of the plane in Anchorage was the cloudy sky that seemed to smother the city. She was greeted by military personnel and ushered to the search command center. There Major Henry Stocker brought her up to date on the search efforts, showing her maps of the search routes and transcripts of the many progress reports filed by the pilots. When reporters crowded around her afterwards, she gave a brief statement. She was 'very hopeful' that her husband would be found alive, she said. Outside the clouds continued to thicken.

> FOR BOGGS, BEGICH SPECIALIST JOINS SEARCH' by Paul Anderson Anchorage, Alaska *(UPI)* The Air Force's top search and rescue specialist was on the scene today as the hunt for the missing plane carrying House Majority Leader Hale Boggs and three others went into its ninth day....'

The day after the plane disappeared, Pegge Begich woke her children for school and told them each what had happened. She had been up all night worrying about her husband and wondering if she should let the children know. Reasoning that they would probably hear the news soon enough, she decided they should hear it from her first. She let them decide whether or not they felt like going to school. She explained that there might be reporters, possibly questions. All of the children listened. All of them chose to go to school.

On the way to James Fennimore Cooper Junior High School, Nick and Tom Begich stopped to rest on a stone bridge. Searching the sky and spying a cloud formation, Tom grabbed his older brother's arm.

'Look! See that cloud? It's like a plane. And that one? It's a mountain.' He waved his fingers at the clouds. 'It means Dad must have made it through. He's all right!'

Nick glanced at the sky and, with his jaw fixed, started walking towards the school. Tom hesitated, then followed. In the sky the plane and the mountain returned to the clouds.

> MS. PEGGE BEGICH RETAINS ALASKAN OPTIMISM, by David R. Bolt, the *Washington Post*'People who don't understand Alaska don't understand why we're not falling apart at the seams,' says Pegge Begich, whose husband, Rep. Nick Begich, has been missing somewhere in Alaska since the light plane he was in went down 20 days ago...In 1970 the entire Alaska Democratic ticket... were lost for nine hours when their light plane flew into impenetrable fog and had to put down on water until it cleared.'

At the Begich-for-Congress headquarters in downtown Anchorage, Margaret Pojhola and Gene Kennedy did what they could to keep the campaign workers cheerful and the campaign going. It was a difficult task in the face of fading optimism.

The recent actions of some Republicans and Democrats, demanding that Nick's name be removed from the upcoming general election ballot, had shocked and crushed Kennedy in the wake of the disappearance. There was a feeling of hopelessness everywhere. Margaret sat down next to him half-smiling at the thought that had just passed through her mind. 'If he comes back, Kennedy,' she said, 'and you've lost this election for him, he'll kill you!' Gene smiled at the thought of a raving Nick Begich and for the moment it lightened his mood. He returned to work.

> BEGICH RE-ELECTION SEEN
> Washington *(UPI)* 'Congressmen Hale Boggs and Nick Begich have been missing since their plane disappeared in Alaska Oct. 16, but the names of both will appear on ballots today....'

The young reporter, Howard Weaver, had been sent to the Begich headquarters for an election night story. He'd been assigned to write a piece on the people of the campaign, the personal story of a campaign headquarters where the candidate likely to win was as likely no longer alive. Politely he asked if he could sit in the main room of the building and take notes. Margaret and Gene assented, but the thought of some young reporter cranking out an election-night hack job was almost too much for them to bear. Weaver was treated icily, his presence barely tolerated.

When the results had confirmed Begich's re-election, Weaver thanked the two and left to file his story. Later that evening Kay Fanning, publisher of the *Anchorage Daily News*, appeared with a copy of the next day's edition. The campaign staff read Weaver's article and were stunned. It was beautiful. With a keen sense of his subject, Weaver had reached into the heart of his story and painted a portrait of despair brightened with the irony of the successful re-election and the bravado of the campaign staff. That morning, in the eyes of Kennedy and Pojhola, Howard Weaver reached a plateau of respect few reporters could ever hope to attain.

After thirty-nine days the air search, the largest in Alaska history, was abandoned. On what would have been Nick's 16th wedding anniversary a presumptive death hearing was held in Anchorage. Two days later, on December 31, 1972, after twenty minutes of deliberation the following statement was issued by the six jurors:

'We the jury, after hearing and considering all the evidence presented, each find that it may be fairly presumed that Nicholas J. Begich has suffered death.'

The Cessna 310 carrying Nick Begich, Hale Boggs, Russ Brown, and Don Jonz was never found."5

On Tuesday, June 26, 2001, and several times since, The History Channel has aired a one-hour *History's Mysteries* segment called "Alaska's Bermuda Triangle". It explored the disappearance as a possible conspiracy citing the 1992 *Roll Call* article that quoted government records that described the location of the plane and stated that there were two survivors shortly after the plane disappeared. The information indicated an undisclosed "firm" involved in testing advanced surveillance equipment had located the crash site. The informant had a military background, according to the FBI document obtained by *Roll Call*. The FBI telex was sent to the Washington, D.C. FBI headquarters where it was presumably passed to the Acting Director, L. Patrick Gray.

The previous director, J. Edgar Hoover, had been in a significant conflict with Boggs, who called for his resignation on the floor of the Congress. Boggs was one of the most powerful people in the country at a time when misuse of power was just beginning to be seen, culminating in the resignation of the President of the United States, Richard Nixon. A good deal remains untold from this period of the country's history and perhaps my father's story being released will compel someone to come forward with the rest of the story.

Some of the other interesting points surrounding the disappearance include the fact that Boggs was taken to the airport for the first leg of the trip by a young democrat named Bill Clinton who later, as President, appointed Congressman Boggs' wife Lindy to the position of US Ambassador to the Vatican. This appointment was after she was elected and served eighteen years in the US Congress following her husband's disappearance. My father had just completed his first Congressional term and, as a freshman, had engineered the biggest cash and land transfer to native Americans in the history of the United States – over 44 million acres and nearly $1 billion was transferred. This transfer and "settlement" was needed for establishing a clear title for the right-of-way of the Trans-Alaska Pipeline, which was then built supplying up to 25% of US oil for much of the time since its

5. Begich, Thomas S. *Second Term: The Life Of Nick Begich.* 1982 limited publication. EPI3556

completion. His work with Native Alaskans was never completed in terms of recognizing native peoples in Alaska as their issues unfolded in the next three decades. Issues still remain for gaining equity for native Alaskans and accountability in government. Our present work, we hope, continues in the tradition of these two great men who lost their lives in the pursuit of what was right and true.

Things seem to run in cycles. It is interesting when I look at my family's work in Alaska and the work which we are doing now as a result of these early encounters with government. I had always suspected that there was more to my father's death than was revealed over the years. Time is the friend of truth. It seems that these kind of conspiracies appear through strange coincidence and sinister design. Sometimes it is difficult to determine which it is – conspiracy or coincidence.

Needless to say at fourteen years old the loss of a father is an intense and life changing event. For me and my family it propelled us into recognizing the fragility of life. It shaped our recognition of our most valuable possession – time itself and the snapshot of life we truly live. It was then that I realized that we were here on the earth a short time and that we should attempt to reach our highest and best potentials as human beings and then, if so called and motivated, attempt to do the same for others through the work we each do. Now, thirty years later, I find myself fully engaged and still learning.

Earth Rising II – The Betrayal of Science, Society and the Soul will open the eyes of readers to issues and ideas which deserve open discussion. We chose a number of topics for this book and having completed the work realized that much remains to be told. We have picked a few subjects which are believed by the writers to be the most important of the day.

These are used as illustrations of symptoms of the overriding problem which has allowed these situations to emerge. They are the outgrowth of fear, uncertainty and apathy which are compounded by an ever increasing complex world. Some of these very same technologies we report on offer great opportunities in enhancing who we are as living souls if used rightly. In these pages are important issues, sub-themes and personal stories which will educate, motivate and change the way we see the world.

Behind each of the problems we describe is the root – *abuse of power*. Whether corporate, government or individual abuse of power always results in disaster. Mankind now possesses the power to enslave the population through the misuse of technology, destroy the environmental systems of the planet itself or create a world where human beings can reach their highest individual potential. Our trusted systems have betrayed us because people, hidden behind institutions of public trust, continue to remain behind the veil. The veil is the threshold of truth and it must be opened. We have allowed our institutions great power without corresponding accountability. Returning to the roots of our history, our basic shared values and recreating a more transparent government while redefining personal privacy in the context of modern technology is part of the challenge which is ahead.

Chapter 2

Energizing the Seas

"Undersea noise pollution is like the death of a thousand cuts. Each sound in itself may not be a matter of critical concern, but taken all together, the noise from shipping, seismic surveys, and military activity is creating a totally different environment than existed even 50 years ago. That high level of noise is bound to have a hard, sweeping impact on life in the sea.

Regulating these sound sources can be difficult, but one has to start somewhere. Every breath we take is dependent on the ocean. And unless we really understand how that vast system works and take better care of it, it isn't just the ocean that's in jeopardy. It's our whole future that's at stake."

Dr. Sylvia Earle, Former Chief Scientist, National Oceanic & Atmospheric Administration

This chapter requires a special thanks to Robert W. Rand who reviewed this section for technical accuracy. Mr. Rand is a professional consultant with over twenty-one years of experience in noise control engineering and acoustics. He is a Member of the Institute of Noise Control Engineering and the Audio Engineering Society. He has consulted on numerous industrial and commercial projects and has provided expert testimony on several occasions. I met Mr. Rand when we were both guest speakers at "A Symposium: The Navy's High Intensity Sonar. August 14-15, 2000." The symposium was organized at the College of the Atlantic in Bar Harbor, Maine.

Acoustic signals in the world's oceans are causing increased public concern as we gain an understanding of how sound energy behaves in sea water. This form of vibrational energy, *sound*, is being introduced both as a byproduct of modern technology and as a deliberately introduced form of energy. When deliberately introduced into the seas by military organizations the interactions do have significant consequences. The way sound energy acts in sea water, or the physics of the interaction, is what is driving the research without realistic risk assessments in consideration of the biological life that billions of people depend on. Man is quickly advancing our technological deployments into the seas in a way which will contribute to our destruction much differently than the environmental worries of the past. The old threats of massive oil spills, nuclear, chemical and perhaps even biological accidents pale in comparison to what will happen if we continue to allow the sea to be used as a conduit for sonar wars. We have seen the impact of poor planning with limited technology in terms of the old threats. The new wave of technology now possessed by governments and academics has placed mankind closer to what most religious traditions once only reserved for God – control of the environment itself. We can now create a better world or, in numerous ways, destroy the one which we have been entrusted to be stewards over. The seas are threatened in the course of the Revolution in Military Affairs (RMA) as a new silent, cold-war begins to take form.

Over the years Earthpulse Press has been following several developments in the area of electromagnetic warfare. The use of manipulated energy fields as a fundamental building block for new technologies has increasingly drawn the attention of military and civilian scientists. The idea of using energy in its various forms to enhance or degrade military systems has been the focus of much attention. Throughout this book the subject of energy manipulation is explored and discussed from several different perspectives. This chapter deals with the use of some of these new technologies on the world's oceans using acoustic, or sound energy.

According to an unclassified NATO document[6] the definition of pollution has been standardized as follows:

6. "Part 1: Marine Mammal Environmental Policy," NATO Unclassified Document - no date. EPI3341

"Pollution of the marine environment means the introduction by man, directly or indirectly, of substances or energy into the marine environment, including estuaries, which result or is likely to result in such deleterious effects as harm to living resources and marine life, hazards to human health, hindrance to marine activities, including fishing and other legitimate uses of the sea, impairment of the quality of use of sea water and reduction of amenities."

According to the document, standards were evolved but they did not include standards for "energy". Although energy was mentioned on an equal footing as "substances" being introduced to the seas, the quantification of energy as a pollutant has yet to be defined for the purposes of regulation. There are no regulations for energy of any type at any frequency or intensity in terms of the seas whether created from engine noise, sonars, or fathometers. The regulation of energy discharges has yet to be created. The paper goes on to clarify the deficiency of international law as it relates to energy in the seas, particularly sound. The document draws no conclusions of substance and is more of a statement of caution with respect to sound in the seas from sonars.

The issue is avoided because of the need of military planners to advance their work without regulation. In January, 2003, I was told by Dr. Marsha Green that the Marine Mammal Act was up for review and that the military was going to attempt to modify the law so they would be exempt thereby allowing unfettered abuse of the seas. A dangerous precedence considering the Department of Defense record as the largest single pollution in the United States. In a March, 2003, the *Washington Post* reported that the military had announced their interest in being exempt from all environmental regulation using the climate of fear based patriotism as the moment of opportunity.[7]

The Story Begins

In the mid-1990s I received a call from a very irate scuba diver who had been swimming off the California coast when he had an experience with sound he never had experienced while diving. He had observed that the military was testing a new kind

7. "Pentagon says it needs relief from environmental rule," *Washington Post* reporter Eric Pianin, March 7, 2003, reprinted in the *Anchorage Daily News.*

of sonar (Sound Navigation and Ranging) device in his area. The sonar's sound, when injected into the water, was having an effect on sea life particularly marine mammals. At that time we were unaware of these experiments and suggested that the diver begin to record his observations. This was a very different type of sonar because it was not a system for just listening – it was designed for sending sound energy through the water as an active sound generating system rather than just a passive listening system. This was much different from the sonar systems of the past used to measure world ocean temperatures; serve as underwater threat deterrents; and, to detect objects under the sea by listening.

Sonar devices are used to detect underwater objects through the use of sound waves. Active sonars put sound into the water which travels at about 1500 meters per second. When the sound wave strikes objects in its path, part of the sound energy bounces back toward the original source. By measuring the sound speed the distance of the object can be found and by careful computer analysis of the signal, other characteristics of the discovered object can be determined.[8]

Hearing is probably the main sense used by whales, dolphins, and other marine species and is as vitally important to them as seeing is important to people. "Most marine mammals depend on sound as they hunt for food, detect predators, find mates, and keep their herds together in the darkness of the sea. For the great whales and others, much of this activity takes place in the low frequencies, in the band below 1000 Hertz. Unfortunately, that part of the spectrum is also occupied by some of the loudest human sources of sound."[9]

The impact that one of these sources can have on an animal depends partly on its distance. At close range a powerful sound can cause tissue in the lungs, ears, or other parts of the body to rupture and hemorrhage. Farther away, the same sound can induce temporary or permanent hearing loss. And at even greater distances, it can affect behavior, leading animals to swim off course, abandon habitat, stop vocalizing, or turn aggressive. In

8. "What is Sonar?" http://www.sanjuan.edu/schools/arcade/SONARVA.html EPI2585

9. Natural Resource Defense Council, "Sounding the Depths: Supertankers, Sonar and the Rise of Undersea Noise." http:/www.nrdc.org/wildlife/marine/sound/exec.asp EPI2397

addition, any loud noise has the potential to drown out other sounds – calves, mates, predators, food sources – around the same frequency, a phenomenon known as 'masking.'[10]

The use of sound by sea creatures has been a source of curiosity for man and has led to the development of technologies which attempt to mimic or artificially create the same effects. Dr. Christopher Clark of Cornell University and one of the principal investigators in both ATOC and LFAS (sonar studies) mammal studies was quoted as saying that the Navy had once asked some scientists, "If you had a sound source that sounded like a blue whale voice, what would you be able to do with it?" According to Clark the unanimous answer of the scientists was that it "could illuminate an entire ocean basin."[11] Mankind through observation often attempts to recreate what nature does so elegantly – such is the case with new underwater active sonars.[12] The objective of the United States Navy is to deploy active sonars in about 80 percent of the world's oceans.

Regulation of sound in places where people live and work is not a new concept but one which has been around for a significant amount of time. Virtually every local community, state and modern nation have sound level standards (on land and in the air) to prevent hearing loss, negative health effects and to maintain quiet neighborhoods. In 1974 the United States Environmental Protection Agency (EPA) issued a report that outlined safety levels.[13] Essentially all of the standards which have been put in place are designed to effect places where people and other creatures live on the surface of the earth. There are no standards for "safe" sound levels in the oceans of the world. The risk to marine life was indicated by the Office of Naval Research, Marine Mammal Science Program released a report in 1999 which

10. Natural Resource Defense Council, "Sounding the Depths: Supertankers, Sonar and the Rise of Undersea Noise." http:/www.nrdc.org/wildlife/marine/sound/exec.asp EPI2397

11. "Is Spreading Sonar Smart Science or Overkill?," by Stephanie Siegel, CNN Interactive, July 2, 1999. EPI2215

12. "Workshop on Broadband Sonar Solutions for Littoral MCM," August 4-6,1998 sponsored by the Office of Naval Research. Dr. Randy Jacobson, Dr. Robert Gisiner, Dr. Harold Hawkins and Dr. Teresa McMullen. *Wide Band Signal/Array Processing and Animal Sonar.*by Richard Altes, Chirp Corporation, LaJolla, Caif.EPI2634

13. www.nonoise.org/library/levels74/levels74.htm

indicated there may be risks to marine life as a result of new underwater sound sources.14

Should there be standards? What are the effects of sound in the seas and does it really matter? This chapter describes the effect of sound in the seas and the potential impact on marine life and people. Like many new technologies these new sonars use nature's normal attributes as extensions for mankind's technology. The exploitation of the earth's normal energy exchange systems is what many new technologies seek to accomplish in fundamentally risky and dangerous ways. Taking what only nature could accomplish as delicately as the formation of a feather man can now create with the energy of an explosion.

Human Health Effects

The risk to people from high intensity underwater sounds is being reviewed by the Navy, NATO and others. Some of the research projects the Navy initiated are listed in the FY1998 Naval Submarine Medical Research Laboratory programs as "Current Important Programs." Little is revealed. The Navy lists the following two studies:

"**Low Frequency Active Sonar:** Tactical use of low frequency active sonar (LFA) may result in unintentional exposure (ensonification) of recreational divers. This study assesses diver aversion and panic reaction to elements of the LFA signal in order to create exposure guidance and an environmental impact statement."

"**Vibration Bioeffects of Low Frequency Sound on Divers:** This project investigates the bioeffects of low frequency sound on divers. In presence of low frequency underwater sound-determines the vibration response of the skull, measures the vibrations in the body structures and measures the psychological impact and effects on diver performance."15

---

14. Environmental News Network, "Impact of Underwater Noise Studied." July 27, 1999. EPI2401

15. "FY98 Naval Submarine Medical Research laboratory, Current Important Programs." http://wwwscitechweb.com/inhouse/reports/fy98/98navy/98navy_activities/98nsmrl/98nsmrl_c.html EPI2643

The studies, if completed to reflect the full range of power intensities envisioned by the new Surveillance Towed Array Sonar System Low Frequency Active (SURTASS LFA), could be proven useful in understanding the risks to humans. However, the same tests may not be comprehensive enough to allow for conclusions to be reached regarding marine mammals and other sea life. Such studies should be designed to be inclusive of other biological life in the seas and not just human exposures. It is unlikely that the tests will be at the thresholds necessary to test the upper limits of the sonars in order to determine the real risks with full use of the new systems. The Navy has misled the public throughout the process by first avoiding disclosure entirely and then failing to run a meaningful set of tests. Hopefully these studies will be inclusive of the full range of possible exposures so that both humans and sea life can be protected and not destroyed by the operation of the technology. The sea, and the life within it, is critical to all life systems on the earth including human life. These life sytems do not operate alone and without interaction between them.

A NATO report[16] which reviewed some of the risks of sound in the seas suggests that "as a general rule of thumb, the sound level at the diving site should not exceed 150dB..." The report was put together to emphasize that the precautionary principle should be applied but fails to define what that principle would imply in the case of sounds in the seas. the "rule of thumb" suggested in the report was limited and contrary to reports of behavioral changes in marine mammals. Again the military organizations disregarded the energy levels where impacts began to be noted and preferred to focus on higher energy levels where tissue damage might begin to manifest. Moreover, they fail to address the impact of resonance in terms of energy exchanges which would account for damage at much lower energy levels. NATO also discusses an exposure limit at the point of reception to be safe at values up to 160 dB[17]. The fact

9. "Part II: SACLANTCEN Marine Mammal and Human Divers Risk Mitigation Rules – Planning." NATO unclassified document, Supreme Allied Commander Atlantic Undersea Research Centre – NATO EPI3342

17. "Summary Record, SACLANTCEN Marine Mammal Environmental Policy, La Spezia, Italy, 17-19 June 1998. Item 20. Supreme Allied Commander Atlantic Undersea Research Centre – NATO

is that certain energy interactions can cause significant biological reaction ranging from mental confusion to tissue damage.

Sound in the Seas

It has been well known historically that sound, as a vibratory form of energy, travels more efficiently than light or other forms of vibrational energy in water. In 1822 Daniel Colloden used an underwater bell in an attempt to calculate the speed of sound in water in Lake Geneva, Switzerland. In spite of their limited instruments in 1822 they were able to calculate the speed of sound in water, which is about 4.5 times faster than the speed of sound in air (1530 meters/second vs. 340 meters/second in air). By the early 1900s this knowledge was being applied in navigation. During World War I sonar systems were just being developed for locating submarines and icebergs with some limited effectiveness. Things changed dramatically by World War II and new sonars were developed which greatly improved the efficiency of these devices. It was also noted that sound traveled differently depending on the amount of pressure created by ocean depth, water temperature and salinity of the water. These factors could effect the sound in several different ways. It was observed that sound could travel along certain undersea pathways with great efficiency because sound could easily flow through these areas with less energy loss and cover much greater distances. It was like electricity flowing through a wire in that the sound would travel along these pathways which were defined by the physics of sound interactions in the oceans.[18] Sound traveling in this way is what partially accounts for whale communications over hundreds of miles as they sing their low frequency song at low energy levels and low frequencies.

When sound travels in the air and strikes a person only about .03% of the energy in the sound is absorbed in the body with the remaining 99.97% of the energy reflected away. This small amount of absorbed acoustic energy, for the most part, is usually considered harmless in terms of its impact of living creatures except when the sound energy is at very high amplitudes such as those produced by explosions. On the other hand acoustic energy traveling in the form of sound in sea water, when it strikes a living creature, 100% of the energy is absorbed and

18 . "Acoustics and Sonar", by John Perry Fish and H. Arnold Carr, AUSS Ltd., Cataumet, MA USA 02534. EPI2388

passes into the animal having a significant potential impact depending on the frequency and energy concentration (energy density). When the energy moves through the tissue of the body it changes speed based upon the density of the material it is passing through. In the case of people and marine mammals when the energy interacts with the air spaces within tissue significant energy can be released, which can cause trauma and bleeding (hemorrhaging). In other creatures microscopic pockets of gases in their bodies can be impacted similarly with damaging effects.

Sound can be characterized in terms of strength (amplitude) or bandwidth (frequency expressed in cycles per second, or vibrations per second – Hertz). The most widely used measure of amplitude, measured by a sound-level meter, is in decibels (dB). Typical conversation speech in air can be measured between 65 and 70 dB. A human ear is capable of hearing a relatively narrow band of sound beginning at about 20 Hertz (Hz), below the lowest note of a piano, up to 20,000 Hz which is well above the highest note on a piccolo.[19] Sound outside of the range of human hearing can be heard by other animal species including many marine mammals.

Sound levels are expressed in decibels (dB) which by definition is a relative unit with a physical dimension and is used to compare power and intensity levels of sound sources to one another. The methods for measuring sound energy in the air and in water are very different because of several factors. When measuring intensity using decibels in the course of this chapter the following information will be helpful:

An intensity ratio of 10 translates to 10 decibels
An intensity ratio of 100 translates to a level difference of 20 decibels
An intensity ratio of 1,000 translates to a level difference of 30 decibels
An intensity ratio of 10,000 translates to a level difference of 40 decibels
An intensity ratio of 100,000 translates to a level difference of 50 decibels
An intensity ratio of 1,000,000 translates to a level difference of 60 decibels
An intensity ratio of 10,000,000 translates to a level difference of 70 decibels
An intensity ratio of 100,000,000 translates to a level difference of 80 decibels

19. Focus: Environmental Health Perspectives Volume 102, Number 11, November 1994. "Environmental Impact on Hearing: Is Anyone Listening?" EPI2404

What this shows is that as the decibel difference increases intensity ratios are impacted. It is important to note that there are standard reference points used to consider sound pressure, which is much different when considering sound in air compared to sound in water. For measurements in water the decibels are given using a standard pressure of 1 microPascal compared to decibels in air using a higher standard of reference of 20 microPascals. This is critical because when comparing decibels in air, which are used to set safety standards in our communities, we cannot apply the same set of standards to the oceans in terms of decibel safety levels. To do so, given the difference in pressure standards, would be like comparing apples to oranges.

What this means is that when the number in decibels increases the intensity of the signal increases even more than would otherwise be apparent by just looking at the decibels. For example in the highest sound energy tested by the US Navy in their experiments in Hawaii and the Mediterranean, the level of energy was significantly below the levels of energy eventually desired by the Navy, according to their own reports. The Navy has indicated that they would like to use the system with a source energy level of 230 to 240 decibels. How does this compare with the tests in the Mediterranean and Hawaii?

Mediterranean upper level at 160dB compared to 240dB
= a difference of 80dB or 100,000,000 times more intense.

Hawaii upper level at 203dB compared to 240dB
= a difference of 37 dB or about 5,000 times intensity difference.

In underwater acoustics source level sound usually refers to the sound level measured at one meter from the source of the sound referenced to one microPascal. The received level is the sound level at the listener's actual position which decreases rapidly with increasing distances between the projector (sound source) and the receiver (sound destination).[20] What this means is that the real effects, when full power is used, will be even more devastating than the tests conducted at 1/5000th of the full power level. Already damage is being done what will happen when 5000

20. http:/www.surtass-lfa-eis.com/UAT&D/index#Sound This site is operated by the Navy and is intended to provide information relating to the environmental impacts of the SURTASS LFA Sonar system. EPI2723

times more power is used? The other important issue deals with the way energy is dispersed and absorbed over distance. While it is true the energy will significantly decrease with distance damage will occur over hundreds of square miles with each test or military conflict where use of these systems will be widespread and the impacts only noted after it is too late.

Comparing sound levels in air against sound levels in water must be done very carefully. First, due to accepted convention described above, the reference pressure values are different by 26 dB. Second, due to the relative impedance (resistance) of air compared to water (the stiffness or density of the medium) or material the sound must pass through roughly a 3,500 times greater power level (35.5 dB) is necessary in air versus water to produce an equivalent pressure level. Combining these two values, a 61.5 dB difference, or correction factor, between the two scales is required. Therefore, 61.5 dB must be subtracted from a sound level in water to produce an equivalent acoustic intensity in air. As explained before, a 60-dB difference represents a million-fold power difference; so it can easily be seen how misleading it can be to try and compare the underwater sound that a system like SURTASS LFA sonar makes with in-air sounds. All sound values are water-standard values unless otherwise specified in this book. 21 The Navy is not clear in describing these correction factors in their public communications and then does not explain the difference in energy coupling described earlier *(only .03% of the sound energy in air being absorbed verses 100% of the energy in water being absorbed into tissue).* The important factor, when making comparisons of what the Navy is asserting as safe, must be recognized in the context of their authorized operating limits. The testing intensity levels are a fraction of the levels these new devices will be used at in the seas if the Navy is permitted to continue. The impact on the oceans and life in them could be devastating based on the military's own testing and established scientific principles. The Navy fails to disclose and debate the real impacts of their tests.

The world's oceans are becoming the casualty of new and dangerous technologies being advanced by the military and others

21. http:/www.surtass-lfa-eis.com/UAT&D/index#Sound This site is operated by the Navy and is intended to provide information relating to the environmental impacts of the SURTASS LFA Sonar system. EPI2723

in search of better weapon systems. Increasingly the use of submarines around the world has become one of the greatest threats to national security. As submarines get quieter in their operation, increased pressure for the development of these new sonars occurs. Quiet running undersea threats have the ability to get close to our shores and, once there, are very difficult to detect. Active sonars are also limited in their operation because of the way their signals travel in shallow water. The problems associated with the operation of underwater sonar in close proximity to the shoreline has become an active area of research for the Navy in their attempt to create effective defense systems. It has also been predicted that within the next thirty-five years anti-submarine warfare capabilities will be limited to close-proximity detections and other limited detections without effective active sonar systems or new detection technologies.22 This is what is driving much of the research as risk is measured against the rewards of undersea exploitation without reasonable accountability.

The US Navy's new Surveillance Towed Array Sensor System (SURTASS) Low Frequency Active Sonar is being promoted by the Navy as safe and effective. Navy operation of this system is expected to continue to advance over the next several years.

The system is designed to operate at between 100 and 500 Hertz. This system has been designed as a part of the Anti-submarine Warfare (ASW) initiatives of the United States Navy. It involves two types of sonar – passive and active. Passive sonar has been used by militaries around the world for decades and involves essentially listening for underwater sound which can be used to locate boats, submarines or other objects. These objects create sounds which travel through the water and can be heard by sophisticated equipment hundreds and even thousands of miles away. This equipment basically "hears" the object and by the way the signal is heard by the equipment it determines where the object is located and what it is. Listening for underwater sounds is

22. *Technology for the United States Navy and Marine Corps, 2000-2035, Becoming a 21st Century Force, Volume 7 Undersea Warfare.* Panel on Undersea Warfare Committee on Technology for Future Naval Forces, Naval Studies Board, Commission on Physical Sciences, Mathematics, and Applications, National Research Council. National Academy Press, Washington, D.C. 1997. National Academy of Sciences. EPI1240

what passive sonar is really all about and is presently considered harmless in terms of environmental impacts. On the other hand, active sonar is a completely different matter. Active sonar creates a sound signal which it releases into the water. The sound, depending on the energy level, can be transmitted for thousands of miles through the ocean where it strikes an object and bounces part of the signal back to the original source of the sound. This bounced signal is then interpreted by computers and equipment operators who determine the nature, location and size of the object.

The interest in active sonar goes back to at least the 1950s with interest in the technology resurfacing in the 1980s with the beginning of the developments in active sonar by the United States Navy. Active sonar is what the SURTASS LFA system is about. The sound signal that is created by the new sonar is sent through low frequency acoustic transmitting source elements called "projectors". The projectors are the devices that produce the active signal or sound itself. The sound is then sent through the sea as a "ping" which can last from about six to one hundred seconds. The ping is a complex set of waveforms which vary in frequency and duration. The signals are generated periodically every six to fifteen minutes during the system's operation.23

The SURTASS LFA consists of a collection of eighteen underwater loudspeakers (hydraphones) each about the size of a bathtub. The array of hydraphones is lowered to between three and five hundred feet into the water below specially designed ships. The speakers are computer activated so that their resulting broadcasts are synchronized to move together forming a relatively narrow beam of sound energy in the water. The sound energy is concentrated when sent through the speakers at the 100-500 Hertz range as it converges at between 110 and 540 meters from the hydraphones. Beyond this point of convergence the sound waves forming the beam of acoustic energy is projected for hundreds of miles first dipping down and then abruptly rising to the surface as the energy is trapped in an undersea wave guide created by the

23 Federal Register: October 22, 1999 (Volume 64, Number 204), Department of Commerce, National Oceanic and Atmospheric Administration, 50 CFR Part 216, pages 57026-57029. EPI2765

natural attributes of sea water in relationship to sound waves.24 This effect of trapping the sound between water layers is what accounts for sound being transferred through the seas great distances.

The modern controversy over active sonars began in the late 1990s when environmental organizations and others began to take note of the new systems and experiments which had been ongoing for at least a decade when discovered. The Navy was involved in several projects which had not been conducted according to environmental laws. The SURTASS LFA system began in the early 1980s at which time the Navy failed to provide notice to the public in the form of an environmental impact statement, which is intended to disclose risks to the public, other potential problems and methods to mitigate or avoid problems. The most significant problem is lack of the Navy's willingness to review current scientific literature, initiate relevant independent studies and evaluate the experimental evidence of the risks in an honest way. The Navy acknowledged the limited scientific research with respect to underwater active sonars and the need for additional studies yet to be undertaken. The need for clarity in terms of risks has yet to be realized. Moreover, they failed to even evaluate any of the risks until forced to do so by the work of activists and US courts.

One of the other issues which has been raised is that the use of an active sonar system actually locates a target for an enemy. Consider that all modern militaries have passive sonars – the kind that listen for undersea sounds. When active sonars are in use they create a signal of such intensity that the location of the active sonar and all US and other submarines nearby may also be revealed to adversaries. This issue has to have been considered by the Navy as it has been raised in the course of the debate on these issues. What does the Navy have in mind to protect the broadcasting source and US submarines as it sends out its sound beacon for all who wish to hear?

24. Natural Resource Defense Council, "Sounding the Depths: Supertankers, Sonar and the Rise of Undersea Noise." http:/www.nrdc.org/wildlife/marine/sound/exec.asp EPI2394

Navy Song & Dance

It has always been a challenge to weed through the public pronouncements of the military when they attempt to hide from the truth through careful wordsmithing. One of the most revealing documents provided by Dr. Marsha Green of the Ocean Mammal Institute was a letter to the Navy from Whale Biologist, Kenneth C. Balcomb, III. His letter was pointed and raised a number of issues important to the debate of the technology and the underlying biological mechanisms which accounts for the death of whales from sonars. He made the following significant points:

1. That the killing was largely due to the resonance phenomena caused when the sound energy passes through the animals' bodies until it passes through air spaces in the cranium around the ears and brains of these sea creatures. The idea of resonance effects are much different than the hearing thresholds being promoted by the military as the measure of safety. What Balcomb suggests is that resonance effects at lower energy concentrations could account for the damage being reported. All objects have a natural way of vibrating. Resonance is the significant amplification of energy when the frequency of an incoming force matches the object's natural way of vibrating. The matching energy increases the energy state of the object cause greater damage than might otherwise be caused if resonance were not a factor.

2. Resonance, he explains, can dramatically contribute to shear forces that can be extremely damaging. After an event like bridges collapsing or buildings falling down it can be explained through physics and mechanics that the effect of resonance is what causes the damage. He specifically asked about the effect of resonance as it related to the LFA sonar, and was sidestepped.

3. In 1998 NATO and the US Naval Undersea Warfare Center had already calculated the resonant frequency of the air spaces in Cuvier beaked whales to be about 290 Hertz which is right in the middle of the frequency range for the SURTASS LFA system.

4. He went on to discuss the impact of resonance as it related to sound in water and in air cavities, including in humans. He pointed out that the Navy, other researchers and scientists could all calculate the effects of resonance through the use of well

known formulas. He points out that by understanding what happens to the air cavities as animals dive and the interaction of the sound energy at the specific frequencies of the sonar, an obvious understanding of the problem begins to emerge. The inclusion of the resonance effects explains the mechanics of the damage.

5. In the concluding paragraphs of his letter he points out the fact that once the resonance effect is considered, the SURTASS LFA system cannot be operated safely. He also expresses the idea that other existing sonars should be evaluated. He further concludes that the use of LFA sonars is similar to fishing with dynamite in terms of its effects.

As a result of a number of organizations targeting Congressional leaders in an information campaign on the new forms of active sonars, a great deal of interest on the issue was raised. The US Navy responded to one congressional inquiry in a letter dated October 7, 1999 by Captain S.C. Miller, III, Head, Undersea Surveillance (N874).[25] In that response a number of issues were addressed in a misleading and incomplete manner. The Navy wants the system and is moving forward without proper consideration of the known problems that will result. By January 2000 the Navy had spent over 350 million dollars on SURTASS LFA making it very difficult to back out of the program.[26] The Navy has made statements (in bold) including the following:

"The Navy is committed to operating this system in an environmentally responsible manner." This statement is not accurate in consideration of several glaring problems. The National Environmental Protection Act, the Endangered Species Act, the Coastal Zone Management Act and the Marine Mammal Protection Act all require proper permitting and compliance by programs which might have environmental consequences. These processes allow for open debate and clarification of risk factors in order to minimize unintentional damage to the environment or

25. Letter dated October 7, 1999 by Captain S.C. Miller, III, Head, Undersea Surveillance (N874) to James H. Maloney, Member - United States House of Representatives. Provided by Marsha Green - Ocean Mammal Institute. EPI2363

26. Letter to Secretary of Defense William Cohen from attorney Lanny Sinkin dated January 18, 2000.

protected species. From about 1980 until 1995 no permits were secured and an Environmental Impact Statement (EIS) was not prepared on this project in violation of United States law. Significant testing and experimentation took place during this time and tens of millions of dollars were expended on the project and its associated research efforts. In 1995 after pressure from citizens and non-governmental organizations a draft EIS was prepared in order to comply with federal law. The EIS was limited in that it failed to address the use of the system at its intended full power. Additionally, it was not until 1998 that the Navy placed the human impacts, as they relate to divers, on their list of priority research projects.27 Now they are attempting to exempt themselves entirely from the law.

"Prior to preparing the Draft Environmental Impact Statement (DEIS) covering proposed system operation, the Navy sponsored an extensive Scientific Research Program (SRP) to specifically evaluate any potential effects." The facts differ from this Navy pronouncement as well in several ways. The "draft" was very limited and failed to address the risk factors when the system is operating at its full energy potential which is many thousands of times more intense than the publicly reported levels tested thus far. Moreover, the testing was limited to four animal species for one month of study. No long-term studies were initiated nor were the studies conducted with the full range of frequencies and energy densities contemplated by the Navy when the system is fully operational. The limits of the testing were so narrow that it is impossible to assert that the system is safe. In fact, based on the limited testing that has been conducted, it is clear to many observers that the risks are very great for significant impacts to life in the seas. The Marine Mammal Commission, a federal agency created to protect these creatures, in their 1997 report to Congress expressed their concerns regarding the use of these new sonars. The Commission said, "If the LFA system were made available for worldwide use as proposed, all species and populations of marine mammals including those listed as endangered and threatened under the Endangered Species Act possibly could be affected." The report went on to

27. "FY98 Naval Submarine Medical Research Laboratory, Current Important Programs."
http://wwwscitechweb.com/inhouse/reports/fy98/98navy/98navy_activities/98nsmrl/98nsmrl_c.html EPI2643

suggest that the following negative effects could result from the use of the system:

- death from lung hemorrhage or other tissue trauma;
- temporary or permanent hearing loss or impairment;
- disruption of feeding, nursing, acoustic communications and sensing, or other vital behavior and, if the disruption is severe, frequent, or long lasting, possible decreases in individual survival and productivity and corresponding decreases in population size and productivity;
- psychological and physiological stress, making animals more vulnerable to disease, parasites and predation;
- changes in distribution, abundance or productivity of important marine mammal prey species and subsequent deceases in both individual marine mammal survival and productivity and in population size and productivity.

"LFA Sonar has been thoroughly tested by not only Navy scientists, but independent marine biologists as well." The fact is that the only testing has been paid for and sponsored by the Navy and there has been no independent verification of any of the test results. In addition, observations made while the testing was being conducted were not followed up by the Navy in accordance with their own project requirements. The observations were not included or reviewed sufficiently by the Navy.

"The marine biologists conducting SRP Phase 1 with blue and fin whales off the coast of Southern California in September-October 1997 observed no decrease in whale vocalizations and saw no pronounced disruption of feeding behavior from whales exposed to received levels from 110 to 153dB. The disruption of fin and blue whales appeared to be more influenced by the disruption of prey than the SRP sonar sound transmissions." This is in direct conflict with the navy's own report on the testing which indicated that the whales had been effected. The chief scientists hired by the Navy noted in their report that whale vocalization decreased between 30% and 50% depending on the species.

"There are no data or information that substantiate the allegations that SRP Phase II testing off the Kona coast of Hawaii in March 1998 led to abandoned calves in the sonar test area." The Navy failed to stop the tests even though reports of problems with calves were noted. Even in the Navy's own report it was stated that abandoned marine mammal calves were reported in the area in at lease three occasions. These were described by all concerned to be very rare events, all of which were reported in the area of the testing.

"There are no data or information that substantiate the allegations that SRP Phase II testing off the Kona coast of Hawaii in March 1998 led to an 80% reduction in humpback whale singing during tests." The Navy's own report on the testing in Hawaii indicated that 10 out of 17 whales tested stopped singing during the testing. Additional tests were conducted by the Woods Hole Oceanographic Institute in Massachusetts and reported in the June 22, 2000 issue of *Nature*. This report indicated that humpback whales' singing patterns were impacted during LFA operations.

"There is no evidence whatsoever that there were any mass strandings near Navy test sites, nor even the remotest indication that SRP testing could be correlated with any strandings." There have been several correlations of strandings related to Navy maneuvers. In 1991 the science journal *Nature* published an article which linked three separate whale strandings in the Canary Islands in 1985, 1988 and 1989 to United States Navy exercises. These were the only whale strandings ever reported in the Canary Islands. Moreover, the testing conducted by the Navy in 1997 and 1998 was thousands of times **less intense** than the energy levels intended for the new sonars. Dr. Alexandros Frantzis wrote an article published in the journal *Nature* in 1998[28] which indicated that NATO testing in the Mediterranean at 150-160 dB resulted in strandings in Greece in 1996. This stranding was ignored in the Navy Environmental impact statement contrary to US law. An additional stranding, not necessarily related to LFA sonar, occurred in the Bahamas in October 1999. This latest stranding was during times when other sonars were active in the areas of the strandings. The physical

28. "Does Acoustic Testing Strand Whales," Dr. A. Frantzis, *Nature* 392: 29, 1998.

evidence deduced from examination of the animals indicated that trauma was consistent with damage from acoustic energy. The Navy finally acknowledged that the stranding of whales in the Bahamas was "most likely" caused by the operation of mid-range sonars operating in the area.

"Some of the world's most qualified specialists in marine biology, and baleen whales in particular, oversaw the SRP experiments. These experts felt that these levels were sufficient to allow extrapolation of results to determine the potential for the onset of nonserious injury." This is not what the experts have said. The tests themselves were at least 5,000 times less intense than the deployment levels indicated in the draft environmental impact statement. The Navy's own report confirmed that "these tests did not use the full source level LFA." The Navy report went on to say that, "it will be difficult to extrapolate from these results to predict responses at higher exposure levels."29

The underlying problem of military research and the connection to funding by the military is a limiting factor for open honest research. The current structures for underwater acoustic research dealing with medium and large projects are virtually all controlled by the Navy and other defense organizations in the United States which effectively restricts academic freedom. The sad story pointed out in *Marine Mammal Science* is the idea that agencies who's main mission is unrelated to science, funds the largest projects effecting marine acoustic environments.30 This problem is not unique to the Navy and is the same problem which reoccurs throughout the defense industry and the agencies of the federal government associated with this type of research. Earthpulse Press has noted throughout our research history that the problems associated with weapon system advancements are routinely hidden under misinformation, minimal disclosure or national security rules which limit access to scientists who would otherwise object. It should also be noted that the military is

29. Letter dated October 7, 1999 by Captain S.C. Miller, III, Head, Undersea Surveillance (N874) to James H. Maloney, Member - United States House of Representatives. Provided by Marsha Green - Ocean Mammal Institute. EPI2363

30. *Marine Mammal Science 11:260-263,* "The US Navy and Academic Freedom." H. & Weilgart L. Whitehead, 1995.

known as one of the worst polluters on the planet. The fact is our military machine has evolved into not only the guardians of national security but, by default, may also have become the gatekeepers of science. Is it wise to allow these bureaucracies to control the information and the use of modern technology? Is is wise to trust institutions which continue to disregard the safety nets established in law? Is it wise to trust institutions which operate in secret without intelligent oversight?

Safety in the Seas

The issue of what is safe is central to the debate on this matter as well as other issues related to energy exposures for humans and other living creatures. Throughout the scientific literature the issue of underwater sound is addressed. It has long been established that impacts to marine mammals begin to manifest at 110-120dB [31, 32] significantly below the Navy's "safe" level of 160dB. At the 160dB level significant damage can be done as shown with the beaching of whales in the Mediterranean reported in 1998 in the publication *Nature*. It was reported by Dr. Frantzis that NATO was 99.9% likely to have been responsible for the beaching of whales using energy concentrations at between 150-160dB. NATO's own research into the incident indicated the exposure levels the creatures were subjected to before they died. The Navy's desired level of 240 dB would be the loudest nonexplosive sound ever put in the oceans with effects unknown at this energy level. The Navy's assertion that behavioral changes do not begin to occur until energy intensities of 160dB is false and not supported in the scientific literature. The Navy however, according to one report, wants to establish the safe level of operation of LFA systems at 180dB which would be at the point where serious physical damage, including deafness, can occur. The level sought by the Navy has little to do with safety and a great deal to do with the operation of LFA sonars.[33]

31. *Marine Mammals and Noise*, 1995, Academic Press.
32. This article provides numerous references to earlier studies of Marine Mammals which were available to the Navy in advance of their testing efforts. "The US Navy's Low Frequency Active Sonar: Cause for Concern," Marsha L. Green, Ph.D., Ocean Mammal Institute, Albright College, Reading, PA., USA. 1999. EPI2361
33. "Navy Noise Policies: Bad Mistake or Worse Strategy?" by Willliam Rossiter, President, Catacean Society International, Whales Alive! Volume IX No. 3, July 2000 EPI2414

The Navy wants the system and is understating the risks in their zeal to use this technology. People in the water will be effected if this system is used at full, or even near full, power in their areas.

The other strandings previously mentioned involved multiple species which are extremely rare under any conditions and the Naval exercises in the area of the strandings remain highly suspect. The major issue with respect to the Bahamas is that the LFA system was not operating according to the Navy yet at least two other sonar systems were operating in the area – systems which the public has been led to believe are safe. The fact that it was already "in use" systems that caused the damage to the whales is even more disturbing because these systems are already in use and are thought of as safe.

The Navy insists that these systems are safe and that, "the United States Navy has used sonars throughout the world's oceans for over 80 years and that there is no evidence that sonars kill whales." This statement is deliberately misleading and gives the impression that all sonar systems act the same way in the oceans. As previously indicated these new sonars are active rather than passive which is a significant distinction. Moreover, the idea that sound energy levels anticipated by the Navy could be reasonably compared to the sonars of the past is like comparing the Wright Brothers first airplane to an F-16 fighter jet – there is no comparison except to say they are both airplanes.

There are significant differences in the types of sonars which the Navy attempts to lump together as if they were all the same. They do not distinguish between military sonars, fish finders and navigational sonars all of which operate quite differently. These three groups of sonars are distinct as was pointed out in an informational press release by Joyce O'Neal and Dr. Marsha Green of the Ocean Mammal Institute in May 2000. The following distinctions were made:

1. The output power of fish finders vary between 55 watts (the energy in a light bulb) to about 600 watts. When electrical energy is converted to sound energy the maximum of 600 watts corresponds to somewhat less than 300 watts of acoustic energy or about 190dB. This high energy level is only reached because the "ping" or sound which is generated is very sharp and occurs

typically in less than 1% of the time the device is activated whereas military sonars have much longer run times or duty cycles where the sound is being generated and sent through the water.

2. In addition, military sonars actually concentrate the energy by the way the signal is processed through an array of several transmitters. The sound is focused into a small area compared to the signal of a fish finder which dissipates rapidly from the source of the sound to become weakened very rapidly at short distances. Fish finders and fathometers are generally pointed downward and the sound might effect marine life but the bursts of energy are short and limited compared to military technologies.

3. The other significant difference between these devises is the operating frequency of the sonar in terms of the signal being generated. It should be remembered that long waves or low frequency sounds can travel great distances through land and water whereas short wavelengths or high frequency signals can only travel short distances in water or through land. The energy in high frequency broadcasts is quickly absorbed and does not travel very far. Most fish finders operate in the 50,000-200,000 Hertz range as opposed to the new LFA systems which operate in the 100-1000 Hertz range, or the older military sonars which operate in the 5,000-8,000 Hertz range. It is the lower frequency combined with the high intensity sonars of the military which adds to their destructiveness and limits their reasonable comparison to fish finders and other civilian technologies.

4. Another significant difference is that the higher the frequency as is the case with fish finders the narrower is the energy beam, even though it can only travel a short distance. What this means is that a fish or marine mammal which is caught in the beam of a fish finder can swim out of the way of the signal in a few moments whereas with military systems the distance to safety is not just a few meters but perhaps at full power, several hundred miles away.

The Bahamas Incident

Between March 15-17, 2000 a multi-species mass stranding occurred in the Bahamas on three islands: Grand

Bahamas, Abaco and North Eleuthra. This stranding involved four types of whales and one dolphin species. The report on the strandings involved some of the best scientists in the field and was reported on by them in a paper later published on the subject.34The significant facts raised in the paper were as follows:

1. The strandings occurred during a thirty-six hour period along a 150 mile arc with the first stranding being observed at 7:30 a.m. on March 15th and with the decomposing bodies of other animals discovered on the 17th of March. Ten of the animals were stranded live and seven were pushed back out to sea. Six of the animals were necropsied (the animal equivalent to an autopsy at Harvard University). In the report of the scientists several factors were reviewed for elimination of causes of the problem including other environmental factors. In the analysis of those animals which were preserved sufficiently for study it was determined that the injuries affected the animals' lungs, auditory system and other related organs.

Stranding of beaked whales in general is very uncommon with only 49 mass strandings between 1838 and 1999 of which 19 were between 1963 and 1999. Of these stranding eight were associated with military exercises.

The combination of factors surrounding the Bahamas event have significant implications. The animals examined were found to be free of chronic diseases or other external trauma. The animals had experienced hemorrhaging within their hearing mechanisms consistent with the kind of damage one might expect from intense pressure events like high intensity sound. It was indicated that it was not the trauma of the pressure event that killed the beached animals but rather death was the result of the effects of the stranding itself. In other words it was not the sonar event which killed the animals it was the act of being forced out of the water which resulted in their death. The report said that "The trauma observed in several of the dead whales is likely to have

34. "Mass Stranding of Multiple Cetacean Species in the Bahamas on March 15-17,2000. This report was prepared by scientists with the Office of Protected Resources - National Marine Fisheries Service; Harvard Medical School; Woods Hole Oceanographic Institute; Southeast Fisheries Science Center - National Marine Fisheries Service and a private veterinarian. EPI2358.

been caused by a distant blast or an intense acoustic event, particularly one with an intense, impulsive profile."[35] The report went on to conclude that, "the most likely cause of the trauma seen are impulse injuries, however the pathological analyses to date cannot differentiate between far-field blast effects and acoustic induced injury." Although the report has not placed the blame on the Navy no other source was located which would provide an explanation for these events which were spread over a 150 mile arc. The problem points to the Navy.[36] Eventually the cause was clearly pointed out as the Navy's mid-range sonar.

The Opposition Mounts

As a result of the various strandings, and the reluctance of the Navy to be more forthcoming in their research, several groups began to mobilize in opposition to Navy testing. This effort became one of the first mainstream environmental efforts which targeted the new technologies being arrayed for the Revolution in Military Affairs (RMA). The idea that mainstream environmental groups would begin to address the effects of energy discharge systems like the SURTASS LFA marks a significant point of evolution for these groups as they begin to realize the impact of modern energy based technologies. The Ocean Mammal Institute operated by Dr. Marsha Green hosted "A Symposium: The Navy's High Intensity Sonar August 14-15, 2000." The symposium was organized at the College of the Atlantic in Bar Harbor, Maine and included people representing the legal, scientific, activists and research communities.

The symposium was interesting and provided a great deal of background information on the issue. I was asked to attend with several other presenters and was able to provide some background on the overall advances of new technology as they relate to the environment. My presentation, was titled, "The Invisible Threat to Life – New Technologies Impact on Living

35. "Mass Stranding of Multiple Cetacean Species in the Bahamas on March 15-17,2000. This report was prepared by scientists with the Office of Protected Resources - National Marine Fisheries Service; Harvard Medical School; Woods Hole Oceanographic Institute; Southeast Fisheries Science Center - National Marine Fisheries Service and a private veterinarian. EPI2358.

36. "Evidence Links Underwater Noise to Whale Beaching," The Washington Post, reprinted in the Anchorage Daily News, June 16, 2000 A-5, EPI1906

Creatures." The presentation included an overview of the new technologies' use of natural attributes of the environment which are leveraged into more effective military tools. The idea of using natural phenomena such as those capitalized by SURTASS LFA has become one of the main areas of military and other academic research. The idea that using artificially stimulated coherent energy sources (rhythmic energy releases) in triggering effects in the natural environment, people or machines is now part of many significant military initiatives. These new technologies can stimulate releases of energy, direct natural energy flows, disrupt normal environmental energy exchanges or cause significant energy transfers with devastating effects on living creatures, other natural systems or property.

The controversy continued to build in advance of the Navy's announced tests off the coast of New Jersey scheduled for May 22, 2000. The National Marine Fisheries Service asked the Navy to cancel the tests. As the opposition made the facts known, the Navy began to back off and canceled its New Jersey testing trial planned for FY2000.[37][38]

Another significant set of issues was raised by attorney Lanny Sinkin a presenter at the earlier referenced conference and author of "The US Navy's $100 Million Mistake: Low Frequency Sonar and the Health of the Oceans." Mr. Sinkin points out a number of very important issues regarding the legality of testing the SURTASS LFA system outside of accepted boundaries. He addresses the fact that under the National Environmental Protection Act (NEPA) it is forbidden to expend irreversible or irretrievable funds on such projects without first preparing an Environmental Impact Statement (EIS). Under Presidential Executive Order 12114 the Navy was also required to prepare an overseas environmental impact statement (OEIS) if the project would impact common ocean areas, a foreign nation or other global resources. Sinkin pointed out that the LFA project had been operating and advancing for over ten years without an EIS or OEIS and that the system was intended to impact over 80% of the

37. "Navy Abandons Controversial Sonar Test," May 28, 2000, The Orange County Register, Associated Press Story. EPI 2392

38. "Navy Calls off Sonar-System Tests After Concern for Marine Life," By Marc Kaufman, The Washington Post, reprinted in The Anchorage Daily News May 27, 2000 EPI 1910

world's oceans. Throughout the report it was pointed out that the Navy had ignored or discounted their own scientists' concerns. The relevance of the testing, considering the difficulty in projecting the results in light of the much higher energy intensities anticipated by the Navy, remained a concern which has never been addressed by the Navy.39

In a report to the International Whaling Commission the Standing Working Group on Environmental Concerns (SWGEC) agreed to prepare a report which would summarize the impacts of environmental factors on whales. Beginning on page 13 of that report the issue of noise as it relates to LFA was discussed as a growing area of concern and one which required close attention. The report was put together in 1999 and 2000 again amplifying increasing concerns over military sonar systems and associated noise generation in the world's oceans.40

Other Related Ocean Initiatives

Several other issues have been raised, in the course of investigating these new sonars. The idea that filling the oceans with high intensity sound for defense purposes could be seen as a good idea is surprising. The lack of consideration of the risks the military is willing to take is the result of limited oversight. The issues are not new. The testing of military hardware and defense technologies has been conducted without sufficient consideration of environmental factors for years. There have been many revelations about the problems created by nuclear testing, chemical and biological testing in the past. The new technologies make other weapons of mass destruction pale in comparison to the power of these new systems and must be more vigorously pursued by political leaders and activists in balancing national defense issues and issues of environmental survival.

New energy weapons which can alter natural systems on a scale never before possible are here now and this new sonar system is but a small part of that larger initiative. A major part of

39. "The US Navy's $100 Million Mistake: Low Frequency Sonar and the Health of the Oceans." by Lanny Sinkin EPI2365
40. "Prototype State of the Cetacean Environment Report (SOCER)," Standing Working Group on Environmental Concerns of the International Whaling Commission's Scientific Committee. 1999-2000. EPI2359

the story needs to be understood in the form of new technology and new environmental/human risks. Mankind is advancing the development of some of the most dangerous technologies in the world. These technologies have begun to show themselves and will continue to advance. Much of the environmental movement is still stuck in the past preferring to stay with those issues which they are most familiar with while other new threats present themselves. In a few instances projects have been uncovered that have gained the attention of traditional activists. These new technologies are becoming increasingly visible as testing and deployment efforts advance. Since the early 1990s these issues began to reach segments of the political right because of their implications. The political left began to object to the new technologies because of other reasons and are just beginning to assess the wider implications of the Revolution in Military Affairs. Under the new Bush administration a desire to "leap-frog" ahead to the new revolution has been announced and is underway while being mirrored by our traditional national adversaries. The race is on again and the world will be its victim.

Some of the other systems which will be used with SURTASS LFA as complementary technologies include the Air Deployable Active Receiver (ADAR) which is a sonobuoy designed to be dropped from the air into the sea. This device would float in the sea and be a passive device used to pick up echoes from active sonars interacting with undersea objects. This device is being tested in conjunction with the Advance Extended Echo Ranging R & D Program which is examining both long-range shallow and deep water anti-submarine research using active sonars and passive sonobuoy receivers (ADAR). The ADAR system was put in production around 1998 and issued a request for proposals for enhancements on October 9, 1998.[41]

Canada And Alaska

Another technology which could be used in sonobuoys is a new barrel stave projector for broadband sonar applications which can send a signal at 1,500 Hertz at 192dB. This new compact device was announced by the Canadian Defense Research

41. N00-013, Title: Middle Game Localization Utilizing Air Deployable Active Receiver (ADAR). EPI3136

Establishment Atlantic (DREA)42 which has been coordinating its research in this area with the U. S. and its other allies since the 1980s. In fact in a report by that Canadian agency Open-Ocean Surveillance is an area of research with an emphasis on both passive and active sonars. 43 The report describes the Canadian interest in creating similar sonar systems. When taken together, we have often wondered what the body of documentation and its correlations would show if anomalous marine mammal behavior or sea life migration patterns were altered without explanation.

In my area of Alaska the Navy conducted some of their experiments. Here in Alaska where populations can be separated by hundreds of miles, beaching or other strange animal behavior could go unnoticed. Fish migration patterns have been subject to significant changes which can be attributed to many other causes before underwater sonar is considered. Beginning on August 12, 1997 and continuing for 20 days the US Navy conducted low frequency active (LFA) sonar tests in the Gulf of Alaska. The tests were conducted about 300 miles southwest of Kodiak Island. The LFA sonar system tested was the 100-500 Hertz SURTASS LFA system. Divers were advised that the signal would at times sound like whale calls. 44 On November 2, 1999 Governor Tony Knowles' office in Alaska released its Final Consistency Finding for SURTASS LFA SONAR DEIS, State I.D. No. AK 9909-01JJ. This decision authorized the use of SURTASS LFA in Alaska waters without so much as a public whimper in terms of discussion by the environmental community in Alaska. The decision indicated that the sonar would be operated at 180dB outside of 12 nautical miles of any Alaskan coastline or anywhere marine mammals were detected within the 180dB zone. It was further limited to 145dB in the area of dive sites. Exempt from the limits were operations during "heightened threat conditions" and during armed conflict.45

42. "Electro-magnetics Section." EMO199, DREA Defense Research Establishment Atlantic. Canadian National Defense.

43. "Surveillance Acoustics." UA0399, DREA Defense Research Establishment Atlantic. Canadian National Defense.

44. "What's New @ DAN: US Navy Announcement. US Navy Announces Advisory in the Gulf of Alaska." EPI 2551

45. Final Consistency Finding for SURTASS LFA SONAR DEIS, State I.D. No. AK 9909-01JJ, November 2, 1999. EPI2542

In Alaska over the last several years there have been many occasions were salmon migrations, whale migrations or other predictable sea life cycles or activities failed to appear as expected. There could be several reasons for these disruptions in expected behavior. Behavior changes in some marine mammals, at a fraction of the 180dB levels of the Alaska SURTASS LFA experiments, have been reported. In the Cook Inlet area of Alaska where I live and worked as a Tribal Administrator, and now Tribal Planner, for the Chickaloon Village Traditional Tribal Council the issues of alterations in returning fish stocks and marine mammal levels are matters of great concern. The dependence of the people of this area on marine mammals as a matter of health and culture remains important. In addition, the need to have consistent supplies of fish stocks is also vital. The coastal area of Alaska remains one of the most productive areas for fish resource harvests on the planet. The use of these new sonars and their potential impact on resources may represent greater risks than the oil industry or other human activity so closely monitored by the dozens of groups active in Alaska environmental issues. In the past other energy related environmental experiments have been initiated and continue to operate in Alaska without significant oversight. The idea that this system would be allowed to operate without consideration to the objections raised in other areas is disheartening, particularly considering the losses of many of the state's sea resources through migration pattern interruptions already being sustained. Could these sonars also be contributing to the problems being reported around the state in recent years?

North Pacific salmon migrations have been disrupted over the last several years. The cycle of salmon is from their fresh water birth streams to their route through the North Pacific until it is time to return to their place of birth to begin the cycle of life again. The routes have become well understood for many streams and regions of Alaska. The way these sea creatures find their way has been associated with sunlight, natural magnetic field lines and their sense of smell.[46, 47, 48] It is also well known that many sea

46. "Salmon Use Sun, Familiar Smells as Guide Back to Birthplace." by Ross Anderson, Seattle Times, June 30, 1999. EPI2181

47. "Do Salmon Navigate by the Earth's Magnetic Field? Article 691 by Larry Gedney, November 23, 1984. EPI2187

48. "Magnetic Field Detection in Marine Vertebrates," by Chris Williams and Amiya Khare

creatures have gas pockets down to microscopic size which could interact with various vibrational energy frequencies generated by LFA sonars. Most of the attention regarding these new sonars has been on the impact to marine mammals. However, with the observation of the effect of resonance when related to low frequency active sonars, other species may also be impacted. A more comprehensive review of these new technologies is required.

Another type of sonar is the Air Deployable Low Frequency Projector (ADLFP) which is an active sonar deployed by air dropping the device into the target area for surveillance purposes. The use of sonobuoys was acknowledged by the Navy in the Bahamas where the beaching of several whales occurred. The Navy has said that they have used these devices for over twenty years without any reported negative effects. What they failed to point out is that over that twenty year period science has advanced and the same sonobuoys of the past are indeed quite different than the new technologies now being tested. Looking at the larger picture presented by the new systems should make clear that the signal generated by these sonobuoys is much different than that of fish finders or other harmless devices of the past. The military acknowledged dropping the sonobuoys away from the test area at distances that, at a minimum, would have required that the devices had to have an effective range of 20 or more miles. This type of ranging would indicate that the signal these sonobuoys generated would have to be low frequency and at sufficient energy levels to return a reflected signal which could be distinguished from the background noise in the ocean area. In other words the energy levels would need to be high. In press reports regarding the situation in the Bahamas it was reported that sounds of about 200dB at 6,600-9,500 Hertz would be used, which is significantly different from the technologies reported by the Navy to have been used "for decades". The Navy also ignored the fact that other Navy vessels in the area were using sonars while the fleet was passing through the test area. In the necropsies performed on the dead whales found in the Bahamas, hemorrhaging was noted consistent with the type of shock trauma associated with exposure to high intensity active sonar.[49]

49. "A Call for Congressional Oversight Hearings into Navy's Active Sonar Activities.", Press Release, Ocean Mammal Institute, Joyce O'Neal and Dr. Marsha Green, May 2000. EP12362

Shallow water surveillance continues to present problems for the Navy because of the way acoustic energy acts in shallow water. The energy bouncing around in shallow water creates too much interference for good signal interpretation with present technology. Shallow Water Attack and Localization System (SWALAS) is a research and development program for the 21st century anti-submarine system according to the Navy. Its main components include active sonobuoys and Magnetic Anomaly Detection (MAD) systems which are capable of sensing slight changes in magnetic fields when metallic objects pass over the sensors which are left in stationary locations under the ocean.50

One of the programs also noted by the Navy was the Heard Island Acoustic Thermometry of Ocean Climate (ATOC) project which the Navy said was designed for acoustic monitoring of ocean climate being conducted by the Scripps Research Institute in Southern California. The Navy's real interest was not on climate but rather on the use of new sound sources in sending signals thousands of miles through the oceans. 51 The ATOC project was noted as one of the scientific contributors to the use of these new sonars in the world's oceans. The report developed by the Navy specifically referenced the ATOC project in terms of objectives other than climate change research. Throughout the ATOC project activities the military insisted that it was just scientific research on climate change 52 when the reality was that the military was using this to mask their real interests in undersea communications and sonars. Dr. Peter Worcester of Scripps Institute of Oceanography, one of the principal ATOC scientists, insisted that the equipment used in ATOC was not at all similar to LFAS and that it was only being used for basic science.53 While

50. "ASW Speak - Glossary," PMA-264 SPEAK 102: Glossary http://sonobuoy.crane.navy.mil/SPEAK102.HTM EPI2460

51. *Technology for the United States Navy and Marine Corps, 2000-2035, Becoming a 21st Century Force, Volume 7 Undersea Warfare.* Panel on Undersea Warfare Committee on Technology for Future Naval Forces, Naval Studies Board, Commission on Physical Sciences, Mathmatics, and Applications, National Research Council. National Academy Press, Washington, D.C. 1997. National Academy of Sciences. EPI1240

52. "ATOC Project Delayed (Temporarily) by Dead Whales," by Brent Hall Board Member, Cetacean Society International, Whales Alive!, Volume V No. 1, January 1996. EPI 2413

53. "Is Spreading Sonar Smart Science or Overkill?" by Stephanie Siegel, CNN Interactive, July 2, 1999. EPI2215

we agree that the equipment is different the underlying value of the test results is intended to enhance military, rather than civilian, objectives. It is not unusual that technologies have multiple uses and the public story of Scripps and the hidden agenda of the military can both be accomplished using the information developed from ATOC in advancing LFA sonar systems. The military does not fund science for science's sake no matter how hard researchers who are recruited into military projects wish to believe.

Another program operated by the Navy is the Sound Surveillance System (SOSUS) which is a fixed component of the Integrated Undersea Surveillance System (IUSS) used for deep ocean surveillance. This system involves fixed position sensors installed on the ocean floor. The installation of this passive listening system began in the 1950s and consists of hydraphones (underwater listening devices). This system is installed along coastal slopes under the water and is primarily utilized for locating submarines up to several hundred miles away. 54

Another conference on new active sonars was held in August 1998 in order to establish research approaches to Mine Countermeasures (MCM) using sonars in shallow water environments. These sonars are all active and at present designed to work in close ranges. The goal of the program is to reach greater distances for detection by increasing power levels of active sonars.

Mine countermeasures are being further advanced by technology which mimics the natural abilities of dolphins in detecting objects and determining whether the object is a fish or something else. Scientists at Orioncon Corporation, which is the defense arm of Orioncon Industries, in cooperation with the Hawaii based company Sea Engineering, are attempting to introduce this new technology. Dr. Richard Dikeman said marine biologists have been aware that, "Dolphins have a great ability to do what we call acoustic signal processing, that is, to collect and interpret data gathered from echo returns." Orioncon has been

54. " US Navy Sound Surveillance Systems (SOSUS)" US Department of Commerce, NOAA/PMEL VENTS Program, SOSUS Monitoring System. http://newport.pmel.noaa.gov/geophysics/sosus_system.html#general EPI2396.

able to mimic the same kind of high-resolution sonar imaging that makes dolphins such efficient hunters and apply it to mine detection. The Hawaiian Institute for Marine Biology is supplying advise to both companies in order to bring the science forward. Thus far the system has proven 99% efficient in discriminating between objects in water.[55] The project was funded by the Navy.

Dolphins' utilization of its natural sonar may even be more flexible than thought. In a recent press report it was suggested that dolphins may actually use their sonar to create a stun capability when hunting for food. Over the years it has been reported that dolphins might have this capability which was confirmed by two scientists who videotaped the dolphins while they were emitting their low frequency clicks in order to stun fish. Peter Tyack, one of the main scientific investigators retained by the Navy for their LFA research, disagreed and suggested that the dolphins only use the sonars to locate their prey rather than stun them as the researchers' video evidence implied.[56]

Interest in Environmental Adaptive Sonar Technology (EAST) has been growing in order to increase the distances of the visible battlespace below the world's oceans. In air space missiles and aircraft traveling at very high speeds remain in the military's immediate surveillance areas for increasing periods of time. Surveillance in airspace uses many different detection technologies whereas in the seas, technologies are limited by the medium of water and the natural elements that are contained in sea water. The conventional technologies used in sonar can have as many as 256 selectable operator modes and include up to 400 different wave forms available for transmission. The complexity of the combination possibilities, when trying to adjust for variable conditions, is limited. The new EAST systems would allow specially designed computers to make the adjustments in order to try and better interpret and create sonar signals. It was pointed out by Gough and Dial in their paper on this subject [57] that there were significant weaknesses in national defense related to limited

55. "Dolphin Type Sonar Helps Detect Mines in Shallow Water," *Defense Systems Daily*, January 25, 2001. EPI3152

56. "Dolphins Use Sonic Booms to Kill Prey," by Robert Uhlig, Technology Correspondent, *London Telegraph*, February 1, 2001. EPI2998

57 . "Environmentally Adaptive Sonar," by Edward c. Gough, Jr. & Kenneth G. Dial. http://www.apl.washington.edu/east/smartship.html EPI2728

surveillance possibilities in the seas. These limits are what each of these new technologies seek to resolve. The paper went on to describe a Cooperative Engagement Concept (CEC) where several different technology platforms are integrated into a battlespace surveillance system which gives maximum visibility to Navy commanders called – *Distributive Sonar.* This paper was focused on the fact that as technology advances, the operator decisions can decrease as the image resolution in the seas increases.[58]

Already SURTASS systems are being modified in order to alleviate operator decision making and interpretation of passive sonar observations through increased use of computer enhanced equipment designs.[59] Commonality of design is also emphasized on the same defense contractor site in the case of SURTASS and its allied technology.[60] The contractor is also developing new TwinLine arrays to be used as part of the new SURTASS TwinLine project tested in 1996 with production beginning in 1999 for use in areas close to shorelines. The next generation is expected to be released in FY2003.[61]

Mobile integrated systems for use in warfare are being developed for increased visibility of the battle environment. These systems integrate air and sea activity through central processing systems which give increased image resolution under the sea, under and on the ground, and in the air. These systems are being improved under the Mobile Inshore Undersea Warfare System Upgrade Program[62] which will process active and passive sonar signals monitored in the area using all available technologies. This type of system was used during the first Gulf War.

Governments Begin to Acknowledge the Threat

"Royal Navy anti-submarine frigates are to fire 'warning shots' to encourage whales and dolphins to get out of the way

58 . "Environmentally Adaptive Sonar," by Edward c. Gough, Jr. & Kenneth G. Dial. http://www.apl.washington.edu/east/smartship.html EPI2728

59. Passive Automation EPI2684 http://www.trwiuss.com/pmw182/programs/PassiveAutomation/index.htm

60. Commonality EPI 2685 http://www.trwiuss.com/pmw182/programs/Commonality/index.htm

61. TwinLine Array EPI 2683 http://www.trwiuss.com/pmw182/programs/TwinLine/index.htm

62. Mobile Inshore Undersea Warfare System Upgrade Program. EPI 2667 http://www.spawar.navy.mil/depts/d30/d37/d372/miuw/miuw.html

before operating long range sonar systems. The Ministry of Defense said yesterday that it was looking at ways to minimize the damage to marine mammals from a new sonar system to be deployed by Type 23 frigates. 'We recognize underwater noise can cause damage to mammals,' a spokesman said."[63] The British finally acknowledge their own impact on the creatures of the seas and later by March 2002 the United States ruled out every other cause and reluctantly admitted that damage could occur as it did in the Bahamas incident. Nevertheless, in the aftermath of September 11, 2001 no slowdown is in sight and the efforts of the Navy continue.

Possible Solutions

Solutions to the problems of undersea noise and new technological developments, which can have significant impacts on the world's oceans, cannot be ignored. In the context of larger initiatives that should be developed to monitor new technologies, in terms of their health and environmental risks, these need to be addressed at the local, regional, national and international levels. The Natural Resources Defense Council offered the following recommendations to begin to deal with some of the new undersea threats:

"Formally acknowledge the problem. Until the scale of the problem is recognized and the measures proposed for its reduction are as serious and comprehensive as those taken for other forms of pollution, the problem cannot be solved. It is unlikely that Congress will take these steps before the agencies report the weaknesses inherent in the current system, develop the factual evidence of the problem's scope, and commit themselves within the available law to a broader approach.

Update the Marine Mammal Protection Act. Congress should pass legislation that gives the wildlife agencies power to regulate 'source levels,' the noise that polluters actually generate; rescinds the exemption allowed fisheries for their acoustic harassment devices; revisits the 'general authorization' granted certain scientific activities, which is overly broad; extends any

63. Norton-Taylor, Richard. *(The Guardian)*. "Navy's anti-sub frigates to fire shots as warnings to dolphins." Aug. 21, 2001. *www.guardian.co.uk* EPI3586

noise control standards that arise under the Act to vulnerable populations of sea turtles; and charges the Coast Guard or another competent agency with the task of enforcement.

Set cautious standards. The wildlife agencies can improve the permit system by setting clear, cautious standards, especially at the initial threshold where permits are required; addressing scientific uncertainties by using the most conservative data available; and developing a matrix of behavioral responses that discriminates between significant and trivial effects.

Regulate with habitat in mind. There is much that the wildlife agencies can do under current law to protect marine habitat. They should identify acoustic 'hotspots' – biodiverse, densely populated, or critical habitat that is subject to high annual or seasonal levels of noise; designate critical habitat for endangered and threatened species, as the Endangered Species Act requires; and through the permit system (and other vehicles) prescribe means of reducing disturbance in these areas.

Create marine reserves. Just as terrestrial habitat is secured within a system of national parks, monuments, and preserves, so should our marine habitat. The National Oceanic and Atmospheric Administration should tighten restrictions on activities within our National Marine Sanctuaries; Congress should expand the list of sanctuaries or create a new system with tougher standards of conservation management.

Require Monitoring. Underwater noise levels should be monitored to protect marine life and humans using the world's oceans. Such activity should be by an independent body, free of military influence. Divers and members of the public need to further safeguard those located "over-the-horizon" from military exercises or experiments.

Require appropriate mitigation. The wildlife agencies should fulfill their obligations under the Marine Mammal Protection Act and in issuing permits prescribe 'methods' and 'means' of effecting 'the least practicable impact' on protected species and their habitat.

Ensure the safety of divers. The agencies must adopt standards to protect the welfare of scuba divers, particularly from activities sited near the coast, and must require operators to notify the public through newspapers, diving journals, and other media well in advance of their actions.

Establish an advisory panel to guide research. To provide funding for research of a general nature and to avoid conflicts of interest, members of the Interagency Coordinating Group on Acoustics should create a pool of funding and establish a neutral, expert advisory panel to administer it. Among the research priorities: determining the acoustic sensitivities of baleen whales and other species; studying the cumulative, chronic, and population-level impacts of noise on marine life; and investigating effects on fish, invertebrates, and sea-plants, which have been relatively neglected. The National Science Foundation should provide funding for those avenues of research that fall within its guidelines.

Seek an international solution. The cooperation of the international community in curbing undersea noise pollution should be obtained, first by bringing the issue before such bodies as the World Conservation Union and Biodiversity Conference (which could launch a global study) and the International Maritime Organization (whose approval is essential in matters of shipping), and ultimately by including noise pollution standards in international agreements. A regional agreement among North American states should also be sought."64

The seas belong to all of us and the need to act as stewards can not be overstated. It will be this generation that will decide the fate of the seas and the direction of humanity. Let us all act with care and with thoughtful consideration.

64. Natural Resource Defense Council, "Sounding the Depths: Supertankers, Sonar and the Rise of Undersea Noise."
http:/www.nrdc.org/wildlife/marine/sound/exec.asp EPI2397

Chapter 3

Cell Phones

Over the last ten years our research efforts and publications have been focused on the impacts of new technology on living things, people and the environment. The idea that these could be impacted in profound ways through the introduction of different forms of energy may well prove to be the environmental story of the 21st century. One of the leading new factors introduced at the end of the last century was cell phone technology which is predicted to have over 1.3 billion worldwide users by the year 2005.

Cell phones have been one of the fastest growing industries in modern history. The uses of electronic communications for average people began with the introduction of personal paging systems in the 1970s – expanding into remote telephones and cell phones by the end of the century. Most people today have either portable phones in their homes, cell phones for away from home use, or both. Young people are opting for just cell phones rather than traditional home phones for their personal and business communications. These devices are connecting people in convenient ways as their cost continues to decline with expanded use by larger segments of the world's population. As the use of these systems expands, the impact of their use is beginning to be felt in several unregulated areas. Not only are great benefits being gained through increased use but health risks are beginning to be observed. Personal privacy issues are being raised and significant societal changes are being accelerated as a result of the introduction and expansion of this new technology. The cost of cell phones will continue to drop as the market increases in size and technologies become more capable and increasingly cheaper to operate. Internet and other connections have been added to the remote world of the ethereal office space making us more productive, more connected, more transparent as individuals and perhaps more unhealthy.

Earthpulse Press researchers, and many of our readers, continue to contribute to our research data bases. Over the last fifty years mankind has introduced incredible technologies which have totally changed our lives in information, communication and transportation areas. The latest additions of biotechnology (living technologies), nanotechnology (miniaturization on a billionth scale) and advance computer technologies are quickly merging into a new super-technology which will link biological based materials to machines and information. This merging of technologies offers both great promise and a great opportunity for abuse.

In the following pages we attempt to bring together much of the research and reporting over the last ten years in the area of cell phone and home portable phones. Often in the debate the portable home phone is not mentioned; however, it should be kept in mind that many of these phones are no different in their potential impacts on our health and privacy than are cell phones.

The Health Effects Mount

The idea of health effects from cell phones or other devices has become the focus of much research. The findings are confirming for many researchers who have made observations over the years of the effects of very small energy sources on living things. It has been discovered that small amounts of energy, when delivered in the right way, can have the same effects as a massive dose of chemicals has on the human body. We are discovering that the complexity of living creatures is influenced by the most delicate fields of electromagnetic energy.

It has long been known that the subtle effects of light and color when interpreted by the human eye, result in sight or when a sound wave, which is just another form of energy, is transformed by the ear and brain into sound we can understand. Other forms of electromagnetic energy are not well understood because their use represents new additions to our environment by human activity.

The known effects of electromagnetic fields (EMFs) continue to be reported worldwide. Tests were conducted in China at the Microwave Institute of Zhejiang Medical University which demonstrated the effects of exposure to environmental electromagnetic fields (EMFs) in 1170 subjects. Visual reaction time was prolonged and the scores of short-term memory tests were lower in some high-intensity exposure groups. They also found that these energy fields could also affect the central nervous and immune systems in man. Their data indicated that chronic exposure to EMFs are associated with significant changes in some physiological parameters." 65 In an American laboratory similar results have been reported. The impact on Calcium ions, which are important in maintaining normal health functions in brain tissues, was found in experiments. This may affect nervous system function. Test "results confirm that amplitude-modulated radiofrequency radiation can induce responses in cells of nervous tissue origin from widely different animal species, including humans."66 This small effect has significant health ramifications in people. What has become increasingly understood is that a small amount of energy in just the right form can create dramatic and seemingly disproportionate reactions in the human body. In the case of cell phones this is the first time that, on such a wide scale, a technology has been directly introduced to the population in a way that places this amount of energy next to the human brain.

Another area of concern is prenatal development in mammals. "Pregnant women have been warned to be wary of using mobile phones after it was found radiation produced by the devices caused defects in chicken embryos...US scientists tested mobile phone-style radiation on more than 10,000 chicken embryos and as a result some researchers are urging pregnant women not to use the phones until the risks can be properly assessed. British mobile phone specialist Roger Coghill said the findings were 'enormously worrying.'"67 "The possible effects of radiofrequency (RF) radiation on prenatal development has been investigated in mice. This study consisted of RF level measurements and in vivo experiments at several places around an

65 Chiang et al. "Health Effects Of Environmental Electromagnetic Fields." *Journal of Bioelectricity.* 8(1), 127-131 (1989). EPI2064

66 Dutta et al. "Radiofrequency Radiation-Induced Calcium Ion Efflux Enhancement From Human and Other Neuroblastoma Cells in Culture." *Bioelectromagnetics,* 10: 197-202 (1989). EPI1864

67 *AAP General News.* "FED: Pregnant Women Warned To Be Wary Of Using Mobile Phones." May 1, 1999. EPI1880

'antenna park.' At these locations RF power densities between 168 nW/cm2 and 1053 nW/cm2 were measured. A progressive decrease in the number of newborns per dam (birthing) was observed, which ended in irreversible infertility."[68] The question is always raised, "people are not mice?" While this is of course true the effects on cells, DNA and other factors are very similar and quite useful in scientific research in these areas. Other research has shown possible immune system responses to very low energy concentrations as well.[69] What has been shown is that very small amounts of energy can trigger chemical reactions in the body which have a significant impact on health.

"Australian research has found one of the strongest links between cell phones and cancer. Over periods of 9 to 18 months, exposed mice had twice the tumor rate as unexposed mice. The mice were exposed to cell phone radiation. As reports linking cell phone use to adverse health conditions have been published, attempts 'have been made by industry to hose down the findings with what is called 'The Hockett Defense' (named after the chief Tobacco Institute scientist) who advised his executives to repeat endlessly, 'men aren't rodents'. As one of the scientists commented to me; 'but DNA is DNA'. At the level of normal cell growth processes, human and animal cells act very similar."[70]

The body has to be seen in the context in which it operates. The body is not a closed system but, rather, an open one which exchanges energy with all of the forces around it. The human body seeks equilibrium or its own balance. Energy – energetic interaction – requires a corresponding action from the body. On an energetic level this results in chemical changes, system stress and other interactions which can be either healthy or not so healthy. The "new techniques using low-frequency pulsed electromagnetic fields (e.g. digital telecommunication) have raised the question of interference with the biological system of humans.

68 Dutta et al. "Radiofrequency Radiation-Induced Calcium Ion Efflux Enhancement From Human and Other Neuroblastoma Cells in Culture." *Bioelectromagnetics,* 10: 197-202 (1989). EPI1864

69 Veyret et al. "Antibody Responses of Mice Exposed to Low-Power Microwaves Under Combined, Pulse-and-Amplitude Modulation." *Bioelectromagnetics,* 12:47-56 (1991). EPI1855

70 Fist, Stewart. "Cell Phones And Cancer." *The Australian Newspaper,* May 5, 1997. EPI1884

EEG-data of people sampled under the influence of these electromagnetic fields are altered extremely in the range of *alpha*-activity as well as during after-exposure for some hours. This biological effect is induced by field intensities lower than the given international limiting values. Regarding these results there is the very important question of possible influences, injurious to health for people exposed to pulsating electromagnetic fields, especially by operating the new type of digital telecommunication networks (GSM-standard)." 71 In each of these observations a very limited area is reviewed involving a few wave forms, frequencies and carrier modulations in a sea of possibilities. Each of these tests represent a look at the beach – a grain of sand at a time. Some energy fields are healthy and are being used to create solutions to many health issues while others are life threatening. Unfortunately good science is betrayed when research areas are disconnected. These disconnects between technological fields are beginning to dissipate as communication increases between disciplines but their resulting precautionary conclusions are going unheeded.

There has been a great deal of laboratory research into the biological effects of EMFs in recent years. It has been shown that even fairly low levels of electromagnetic radiation can change the human body's sleep rhythms, affect the body's cancer fighting capacity by harming the immune system, and change the nature of the electrical and chemical signals communicating between cells.72 The research has shown that this energy may also contribute to Alzheimer's disease. "These results are consistent with previous findings regarding the hypothesis that electromagnetic field exposure is etiologically associated with the occurrence of Alzheimer's disease."73

Reports continue to amplify the same results which are being replicated now around the world. At the same time the industry is shifting the standards changing cell phone designs and altering other factors which make evaluation of the effects even

71 Klitzing, L. von. "Low-Frequency pulsed electromagnetic fields influence EEG of man." *Physica medica,* April 28, 1995. EPI1863

72 *ARRL Handbook for Radio Amateurs.* "RF Radiation and Electromagnetic Field Safety." 1996. EPI1980

73 Sobel et al. "Electromagnetic Field Exposure and Alzheimer's Disease." *Neurology,* Dec. 1996. EPI1800

more difficult. "Existing data indicate that RFR of relatively low intensity (SAR < 2 W/kg) can affect the nervous system. Changes in blood-brain-barrier, morphology, electrophysiology, neurotransmitter functions, cellular metabolism, calcium efflux, and genetic effects have been reported in the brain of animals after exposure to RFR. These changes can lead to functional changes in the nervous system. Behavioral changes in animals after exposure to RFR have been reported."[74, 75] New research indicates that exposure to cell phones' radiation causes red blood cells to leak hemoglobin, the build up of which can cause heart disease and kidney stones. Scientists exposed samples of blood to microwave radiation and found that even at lower levels than those emitted by cell phones, the blood cells leaked hemoglobin. "Last month, scientists at Sweden Lund University found that two minutes of exposure to emissions from mobile phones can disable a safety barrier in the blood causing proteins and toxins to leak into the brain. This can cause the chances of developing diseases such as Alzheimers, multiple sclerosis and Parkinsons to increase. Symptoms reported by mobile phone users include fatigue, dizzy spells and memory loss."[76] These disorders are increasing in people and taking a toll on all segments of society in their impacts to individuals and families.

British scientists are demanding that mobile telephones carry a health warning. "Amid an explosive growth of mobile communications, concerns are mounting about cellular telephones' potential links to health problems ranging from headaches to brain tumors...Mobile telephones are arguably the most radiative appliance we have ever invented apart from the microwave oven and people are putting them by their heads – arguably the most sensitive part of the body," bio-electromagnetics

74 Lai, Henry. "Neurological Effects of Radiofrequency Electromagnetic Radiation Relating to Wireless Communication Technology." Bioelectromagnetics Research Laboratory, Department of Engineering, University of Washington, Seattle, Washington. Paper presented at the IBC-UK Conference: Mobile Phones - Is there a Health Risk? Sept. 16-17, 1997 in Brussels, Belgium. EPI1815

75 Phillips et al. "DNA damage in Molt-4 T-lymphoblastoid cells exposed to cellular telephone radiofrequency fields in vitro." *Bioelectrochemistry and Bioenergetics*, Jan. 9, 1998. EPI1854

76 Harris, Sarah. "Now Mobiles Give You Kidney Damage." *Daily Mail*, Dec. 13, 1999. EPI1812

scientist Roger Coghill said. Cell phones emanate microwave radiation, and human brains may absorb up to 60 percent of that energy. One engineer said he has suffered severe loss of short-term memory. He began suffering from twitching eyes and numbness of the head within months after using a digital mobile phone for up to six hours per day in 1995. These experiences also begin to raise the question of liability for third parties in terms of employment hazards which result in long term illnesses. The need to exercise some measure of caution in how much we use cell phones, at a minimum, should be considered. Reducing overall use of the devices is a reasonable precaution all can use.

Standard setting organizations are having their own problems creating standards and finding agreement on the levels of risk. One of the problems pointed out by the United States General Accounting Office was that testing was not standardized and that results could vary. They said that identified exposure levels could vary by up to sixty percent and that the Federal Communication Commission (FCC) was having difficulty recruiting the necessary expertise to manage the regulations and develop real applicable standards.77 This creates a problem in that industry claims are accepted without consideration of testing variables based on the testing method followed. The National Radiological Protection Board (NRPB) that sets the standards for exposure in Britain has similar problems in setting standards. "Recommended radiation limits are measured in 'specific absorption rates' – the amount of radiation averaged over one gram of tissue." The NRPB recommends a limit of 10 milliwatts per gram, though proposed European guidelines are five times more restrictive."78 The need for the right level of expertise to be connected to the standards is proving universal both because of the fact that the communi-cations are not uniformly regulated and safeguarded in terms of security and privacy as well as health and safety exposures related to radiation levels emitted from the use of the technology. When these technologies are considered in terms of wireless connectivity which is being introduced increasingly in every area even greater impacts will be felt. These new unseen

77 General Accounting Office, "Telecommunication - Research and Regulatory Efforts on Mobile Phone Health Issues." GAO-01-545, May 2001 Report to Congressional Requesters, United State Government. EPI3348

78 Ridley, Kirstin. "British Scientists Demand Cell Phone Warnings." *Reuters*, Jan. 1, 1998. EPI1788

energy fields will increasingly permeate our living environments without a well defined threshold of safety being applied that is in line with the most current research in the related fields of health.

How much evidence on the risks of mobile phones must be shown before the industry admits to the risks? "Scientist Clas Tegenfeld who is writing a book on biological effects of electromagnetic fields is pessimistic: 'Already there are at least 15,000 scientific reports on the subject. I am afraid the truth is that we don't want to know.'"[79] The "head in the sand" syndrome will not make the problem go away and it must be dealt with by the scientific community, regulatory agencies and other non-governmental organizations. Other reports have also indicated that there may be risks to brain function. In one study the "results show that even a short exposure to the electromagnetic fields emitted by cellular telephones can affect brain physiology."[80]

Children may be more sensitive to microwaves than adults with an Australian report indicating they absorb microwaves at 3.3 times the rate of adults with digital phones more dangerous than analog phones because digital phones emits a pulsed signal. "For amplitude or pulse-modulated RF fields, there is the implication that some form of envelope demodulation occurs in tissue recognition of ELF modulation components, but the tissue remains essentially transparent to the same signal as an unmodulated carrier."[81] Extremely Low Frequency (ELF) signals have been reported to stimulate physiological responses in many experiments where in certain exposures there was an effect but in others not manipulated in the same way there was no effect at all. It could be compared to the dialing of a radio signal – if slightly off the signal is not clear. Yet when there is clear resonance between the transmitter and the receiver the signal is clear. The

---

79 Frey, Allan H. "Headaches from Cellular Telephones: Are They Real and What Are the Implications?" *Environmental Health Perspectives,* March 1998. EPI1803

80 Petrides, Michael, *In Focus Neuroreport Vol II No. 15,* "Exposure to Electromagnetic Fields by Using Cellular Telephones and its Influence on the Brain", October 20, 2000. EPI2770

81 Adey, Dr. W. Ross. "Cell And Molecular Biology Associated With Radiation Fields Of Mobile Telephones." Dept. of Biochemistry, University of California, Riverside. EPI1857

same is true in the human body. Someday it will be as well understood as radio science. It will be commonly known and understood that we can dial up the health of a person and either tune or harm the body depending on the knowledge and intent of the equipment operator. Research is showing that the body can be both monitored and influenced by measuring signals from the body and conditioning signals entering the body. This area of science is advancing the understanding of human health sciences.

There have been reports of headaches.[82] Evidence from the 1960s and 70s supports the conclusion that cell phones cause headaches among some users. Cell phone "transmitting frequencies fall in the most sensitive band for the microwave hearing effect. The transmitting frequencies are also in the band that has maximal penetration into the head. Further, when the head is shielded from the microwave energy, the area of the head that needs to be exposed to the microwaves in order for people to perceive the effect is in proximity to the antenna of present day cellular telephones," research scientist Dr. Allan H. Frey wrote. The most important point that came out of his microwave research in the 1960s was that his human subjects were reporting headaches. Thirty years ago Frey encountered and reported headaches from microwave energy exposure at approximately the same frequencies, modulations and incident energies that present day cellular telephones emit.[83] Dr. Frey was involved in several research areas related to the concept of microwave hearing or the act of creating audible signals inside the head without a physical connection to a device or without using the normal hearing channels via the ear. This may one day lead to the development of new concepts of wireless communications. These types of communications have been researched and will likely emerge into the mix of new technologies in the coming decade.

Already significant research has been initiated in the area beginning with the early work of 1950s-60s researchers. The work of German researcher Robert Thiedemann of Munich has significantly advanced the earlier work creating a sound transfer

---

82 Frey, Allan H. "Headaches From Cell Phones: Are They Real?" E-mail published on *microwavenews.com.* EPI1856

83 Frey, Allan H. "Headaches from Cellular Telephones: Are They Real and What Are the Implications?" *Environmental Health Perspectives,* March 1998. EPI1803

device superior in performance to earlier sound transfer devices such as those created by Flanagan Technologies and others. As these words are being written the newest generation of electronic sound transfer devices are being evolved and beta-tested prior to a 2003 release to the public of the *Earthpulse Soundwave*™. The new device will pass sound through the body directly to the auditory parts of the brain using 21st century engineering, technology and signal generators which may take the new device orders of magnitudes above past inventions. This sound transfer device as it continues to advance may have profound implications for the deaf community as an alternative to more invasive corrective procedures.

The Gift Betrayed

One of the underlying themes within this book is betrayal – *betrayal of science, society and the soul.* Sometimes betrayal is deliberate, sometimes subtle and elusive, and sometimes the result of neglect and misdirection. The gift of creativity in all of its incredible human forms is not intended by the Creator to be withheld but rather, is intended to be shared and developed for the benefit of society and the soul. This is our view of a person's relationship to creativity and it implies a great responsibility to use our skills, talents and creative gifts to improve our own lives and the lives of others.

For some people science has become their outlet for creative expression with a few each decade emerging as leaders in many areas of human expression. These individuals also have a big responsibility to use their gifts for the benefit of humankind in a balanced way. People are motivated by limitless numbers of things, events and experiences which alter the way we use our talents. In science, the greatest betrayals come from neglect of talent in favor of self-indulgence where knowledge is lost or wasted.

A scientist I once counted among my closest friends, claimed he had over 300 inventions created over his lifetime sitting on the shelf. Out of these many ideas only four or five were available to the public as applied developed technologies. He talked about all these wonderful ideas and creations which would be so beneficial to mankind yet he chose to leave these ideas "on the shelf" and even, in those he introduced, he failed to advance and develop them well. It was neglect in favor of self. It was amazing to me that so much could be withheld with no sense of loss or sense of responsibility. That scientist was once one of my closest friends. I saw him transform from a serious scientist to a person immersed in self, who's heart and words no longer seemed connected to his work. I saw my friend change from the person I knew as a serious scientist to someone more interested in entertainment and overindulgence. That friend was Dr. Patrick Flanagan. His potential for contributing to the communication revolution was lost, or at a minimum delayed, because of his personality changes. Changes which were so profound that he became a stranger to me. Creativity always finds an outlet it seems through others who are more rightly oriented as was the case in this instance.

Advancing the Wireless

I met Robert Thiedemann in Munich in 1996 after corresponding with him and his partner, Sabine Fechner, who had read Earthpulse's first book *Angels Don't Play This HAARP*. In that book we mentioned the Neurophone® which was a sound transfer device invented in the 1950s by Patrick Flanagan. The device was capable of transferring sound through the body to the brain where it was clearly understood just like sound heard through a person's ears. The device was reintroduced and we eventually marketed it around the world beginning in 1996. The Neurophone® continued to develop along old lines that did not perfect sound quality or the circuitry sufficiently. The inventor had not kept up with the advances in electronics. Theories and science had advanced in these areas in ways which could greatly improve the technology, perhaps leading to new voice recognition systems and communications systems far beyond the current capability of cell phone communication technology. There is a long story surrounding this device, its reintroduction and uses, but suffice it to say that the device while remarkable was limited.

The earlier Flanagan technologies had stimulated Robert Thiedemann's thinking and began for him a search to improve and advance the technology. He had worked with my organization as a leading distributor of books and products throughout Germany, Switzerland and Austria until 1999 when, for a variety of reasons, research efforts with Flanagan and my organization were halted. At that time Thiedemann was able to follow his own inventive and highly disciplined intuition and discover a revolutionary new technology. In the same way that researchers have had their imaginations stimulated by the earlier work of inventors such was the case with Thiedemann. His new direction has resulted in a breakthrough once sought by earlier researchers and never achieved within the range accepted by regulatory agencies. The leap forward of Thiedemann's research into a technology can be compared to the difference between the first airplane and the modern jet fighter. Thiedemann may have begun the first step in a direction which will deliver on the hope of those most in need of these breakthrough technologies. The wireless world may well be further defined through direct biological system linkages which this researcher is developing. What may in fact someday be possible, should his research effort continue to advance, is a communication technology which would allow for even the deaf to hear. The challenge will be to make sure that these technologies are available for proper uses defined by sensible development of the technology together with the requisite safeguards. We are pleased that we were able to support in a small way the efforts of these inventors in creating alternative technologies which may one day solve significant problems of communications. It is also possible that the greater understandings of sound transfers might impact other areas of science as well.

The EFM Controversy Continues

Researchers have shown that low intensity microwave exposure opens up the blood/brain barrier, a biological effect which can allow the release of dangerous chemicals into the brain. The U. S. Department of Defense stopped open funding of blood/brain barrier experiments that used low intensity microwave energy which is cause for concern. Recognition of low-intensity effects would greatly limit military and civilian exposures. Limiting the exposure of military personnel would have an impact on many of the national defense systems. The problem is again the “head in the sand mentality.” This approach to “don’t know - don’t tell” has proven dangerous in the past with dozens of abuses reported.

"New Swedish research shows that the radiation from mobile phones might make it easier for poison to penetrate into the brain. The findings could explain the diseases that American soldiers who have participated in high-tech warfare are suffering from. The unexplained symptoms of American soldiers of the Kuwaiti (Iraq) war are suspected to link to the medication they took against nerve gas. The microwaves surrounding soldiers in high-tech warfare could have opened the blood-brain-barrier, and the medication penetrated into the brain. The possibility is now being investigated by the US Air Force in cooperation with the Lund scientists."[84] This issue is significant in that there were many different poisons introduced onto the battlefield from many sources in amounts thought to be harmless to the body and health of a person. This is the same in the civilian sector as the advances continue to be made in wireless communications where eventually everything may be electronically connected. As connectivity increases so does our exposure to various forms of wireless energy transmission in many different forms.

"Data in the literature now indicates that the dopamine/opiate system may be involved in headaches and suggests that headaches may be due to cellular emissions...the energy used was approximately the same in frequencies, modulations, and incident energies as those emitted by present day cellular telephones. These current reports of headaches may be the canary in the coal mine, warning of biologically significant effects."[85] The early research by Dr. Frey was most revealing in that it was conducted before the advent of the cell phone. As a result, the research was done with limited, if any, economic impact on industry and the results were unchallenged. Now as the issues begin to emerge there are powerful adversaries who's economic interests are thwarted by the truth of the risks. The industry has gone to increasing lengths to shape and control the common knowledge and perception of the problem repeating for some observers the same scenario as the tobacco industry.

---

84 *Svenska Dagbladet.* "Microwaves open up the Blood Brain Barrier." Sept. 15, 1999. EPI1829

85 Frey, Allan H. "Headaches from Cellular Telephones: Are They Real and What Are the Implications?" *Environmental Health Perspectives,* March 1998. EPI1803

"German investigators report that exposure to electromagnetic fields during mobile phone use may increase resting blood pressure. Exposure of the right hemisphere to a radio-frequency electromagnetic field for 35 minutes causes an increase in sympathetic efferent activity with increases in resting blood pressure between 5 and 10 mm Hg, most likely due to more pronounced vasoconstriction."86

"Mobile phones can cause sudden confusion and short-term memory loss, according to worrying research by British military scientists. Signals from the phones disrupt part of the brain which controls memory and learning, researchers at the Defense Establishment Research Agency have discovered." Project director Dr. Rick Hold said "This is the first real evidence that these sort of radio waves do have an effect on the brain." The researchers found that the "signals made no difference in their measurements for a short time, but then readings plunged off the graph. In a live rat, the effect would have caused sudden memory loss and confusion."87 These problems persist in the literature but the idea of an inconclusive body of research remains in the rhetoric being released by the industry in their public relations efforts.

"Scientists from Colorado University have shown that frequent mobile users had significantly depressed melatonin – a vital cancer-preventing hormone. An Australian study has linked the phones to a higher rate of brain cancer while a Swedish survey suggested that using a mobile phone for more than 15 minutes could lead to headaches and fatigue."88

The most difficult area of research is the complexity of interactions which are possible. Nevertheless a great deal can be gained by looking at the very specific sources of EMFs in determining both their effects and ways to limit human exposure. "It is difficult to deny that RFR at low intensity can affect the nervous system. However, data available suggest a complex

86 *Lancet.* "Mobile Phone Electromagnetic Fields Increase Resting Blood Pressure." June 20, 1998. EPI1823

87 Pryer, Nick. "Mobile Phones Can Affect Memory." *Associated Newspapers Ltd.,* July 16, 1998. EPI1882

88 Coghill, Roger. "Why I believe That All These Items Should Carry A Health Warning." *Daily Mail,* July 17, 1998. EPI1890

reaction of the nervous system to RFR. Exposure to RFR does produce various effects on the central nervous system. The response is not likely to be linear with respect to the intensity of the radiation. Other parameters of RFR exposure, such as frequency, duration, waveform, frequency- and amplitude-modulation, etc., are important determinants of biological responses and affect the shape of the dose (intensity)-response relationship. In order to understand the possible health effects of exposure to RFR from mobile telephones, one needs first to understand the effects of these different parameters and how they interact with each other."[89] As we have increased our exposure to both chemicals and EMFs in the last three decades we have seen certain brain cancers increase in all age groups by 1% a year. Since 1980 those 65 and older have increased 2.5% a year and those over 80 by as much as 500% increased incidences have been observed since 1973.[90] What are the additive factors which have created these statistics? Many individual factors have been analyzed while others remain neglected by science. The fact remains that of all of the manmade factors only a few have been reviewed, and the possibility to address all of the combinations of factors is impossible at present. What is possible and will likely occur is continued evolution of technology and its impact. In the case of these devices and their follow-on technologies, our view of the world will change.

Remote Home Portable Phones

Cell phones are not the only phones to cause concern about health problems. "Today's high-frequency cordless phones may emit a level of electromagnetic radiation similar to cell phones. And for reasons of health and privacy, a growing number of scientists and other experts are dead set against cellphones. They say a cancer risk is associated with signals that have a strong wattage and high frequency (short wavelength).

89 "Neurological Effects of Radiofrequency Electromagnetic Radiation." Bioelectromagnetics Research Laboratory, Dept. of Bioengineering, School of Medicine and College of Engineering, University of Washington, Seattle, Washington. Paper presented to the Workshop on possible biological and health effects of RF electromagnetic fields. Mobile Phones and Health, Symposium, Oct. 25-28, 1998, University of Vienna, Austria. EPI1794

90 Burcum, Jill. "A Medical Enigma - A Rise in Brain Tumors Sets Off Search For A Reason." *Minneapolis Star Tribune*, Jan. 6, 1999. EPI1889

First generation cordless phones operate at about 60 megahertz and the next ones ran at 900 megahertz – higher than 835 MHz cell phones. The new 2.4 GHz is higher still and can transmit for several kilometers without fading."[91] As standards develop these phones will evolve. In all of the research we have done it is clear that the communications revolution, perhaps while offering great promise may also present the risk of great losses. Home phones and wireless will eventually replace many if not all hard wired systems. As the cost decreases, remote phones will become more powerful but likely remain poorly constructed in terms of shielding RF radiation.

Brain Tumors?

"Two new studies have shown links between mobile phone usage and brain tumors. The studies are not absolutely conclusive but the American and Swedish authors have urged users to ration use of mobile phones until more is known. Dr. [Lennart] Hardel's study, as yet unpublished, looked at brain tumor sufferers. It found a correlation between phone use and cancer. His study showed that mobile phone use, regardless which side of the head it was held against, increased the risk of a brain tumor by almost two and a half times."[92] Additional studies were completed connecting brain tumors to analogue cellular telephones with the latest paper presented June 6-7, 2001 at a conference held on the safety of mobile phones.[93]

Dr. Peter French, principal scientific officer at the Center for Immunology Research at St. Vincent's Hospital in Sydney, has suggested that cell phone radiation well below current safety levels could stress cells in the human body in such a way as to increase their susceptibility to cancer. The scientists found that repeated exposure to mobile phone radiation led to the manufacture of heat shock proteins within human cells. The

91 Ebden, Theresa. "Do Convenient, Little Phones Pose Risk?" *Toronto Star,* Jan. 28, 1999. EPI1877

92 Uhlig, Robert. "New studies link brain tumors to mobile phones." *Electronic Telegraph,* May 24, 1999. EPI1824

93 Dr. Lennart Hardell - Örebro University & Dr. Kjell Hansson Mild - National Institute for Working Life in Sweden, "Swedish Study on use of Cellular and Cordless Telephones and the Risk for Brain Tumors," Conference on Mobile Telephones and Safety, June 6, 2001 EPI3394

manufacture of these proteins is a normal function of cells in reaction to stress. It is known that when produced too often or for long periods of time they can initiate cancer and decrease the effectiveness of anti-cancer drugs. Although no absolute link has been established the recognition of the situations has provided a theoretical framework for understanding the factors which may lead to cancer formation from cell phones.94

Some of the leading researchers were contracted by Motorola to carry out some experiments. As two of the world's leading radiation experts they reported to *The Express* that multinational companies tried to influence the results of their research. "Professor Ross Adey, a biologist, had his funding withdrawn by Motorola before completing research which showed that mobiles affected the number of brain tumors in animals. Dr. Henry Lai, who has been studying the biological effects of electromagnetic fields for 20 years, was asked three times to change findings on how they caused DNA breaks in rats."95 Both of these scientists have been involved in academic, military and other research projects throughout their lives. In fact many of their observations on the health effects of EMFs have been used in increasing the military's understanding of these potential weapons applications as reported in our earlier work.96

"Jerry Phillips, who has a doctorate in biochemistry, worked with U.C. Riverside's [Ross] Adey on Motorola-funded research beginning in 1991." He describes a pleasant relationship with them until studies linked exposure to changes in the incidence of brain tumors in rats. "Motorola was adamant that Adey never mention DNA damage and RF radiation in the same breath," Phillips said. "Motorola has been manipulative of research that we and others have reported to them," said Adey. "Essentially they cut us off because we were too inquisitive." Adey found that some frequencies of RFR lessened the incidence

94 Goodwins, Rupert, *ZDNET (UK)*, "Study: How Cellphones Can Cause Cancer", June 25, 2001, http://www.zdnet.com/filters/printerfriendlyy/0,6061,2779684-2,00.html EPI3436

95 Fleming et al. "Cover-up claims over mobile phone danger." *Express Newspapers*, May 24, 1999. EPI1825

96 *Earth Rising – The Revolution: Toward a Thousand Years of Peace.* by Dr. Nick Begich and James Roderick, January 2000, Earthpulse Press Incorporated, ISBN 1-890693-43-X.

of tumors in rats. Motorola was unwilling to recognize this test, not wanting to admit any biological effects of RFR whatsoever. "Phillips, Adey, and others said they see a strong parallel between what's happening now and the decades of denial by the tobacco industry..."

"Though 40% of the energy radiated from cell phones is absorbed by the head, the amount is not significant enough to cause heating. Evidence points to DNA damage as a source of the health problems associated with cell phone use. It is suggested that RFR may hinder the ability of DNA to repair itself."97 "For the first time in history, we are holding a high-powered transmitter against the head,' said Ross Adey, a professor of biochemistry at the University of California, Riverside. When you talk on your mobile phone, your voice is transmitted from the antenna as radio frequency radiation (RFR) between 800 MHz and 1,990 MHz at a range that's right in the middle of microwave territory. Not surprisingly, it now appears that exposure to this microwave RFR may have serious health consequences."98 The research continues with another major study being conducted in Europe. "The biggest study to date into suspected links between mobile phones and cancer will begin this year. Nearly 9,000 cancer sufferers in 14 countries will be interviewed by scientists in a study funded by the European Commission. "Researchers want to establish once and for all if there is a link between mobile phones and brain tumors and other cancers." Results of the study should be available by 2004.99

Microwaves similar to those emitted by cell phones may effect long-term memory, according to a new study by a University of Washington researcher. Henry Lai, a research professor in the UW's bioengineering department, has linked diminished long-term memory and navigating skills in rats with exposure to microwaves like those from cellular telephones."100

---

97 Bass, Gordon. "Is Your Cell Phone Killing You?" *zdnet.com,* Dec. 1999. EPI1792

98 Bass, Gordon. "Is your cell phone killing you.?" *PC Computing Magazine,* Nov. 30, 1999. EPI1813

99 *Sunday Mirror.* "World's Biggest Probe into Mobile Phones And Cancer." Oct. 24. 1999. EPI2061

100 University of Washington. "Rats exposed to cell phone microwaves suffer long-term memory loss, according to new study by a University of Washington researcher."Press Release, Nov. 30, 1999. EPI1795

His research began long before the advent of cell phones and his conclusions were ignored. The pattern continued to repeat itself anytime adverse risks were determined from either new or old research. The justifications of the industry have continued to unravel and the industry has begun to respond. They have not acknowledged the risks but have begun to reduce the emission levels from their phones and have begun to patent protective or shielding technologies. "The world's largest mobile telephone manufacturers have been patenting devices to reduce the risk of brain tumors among users while rejecting claims of any health hazards."101 The three leading manufacturers Nokia, Ericsson and Motorola have all filed patents for components designed to reduce emissions. Some of the patents indicate that the companies have been working on the problem at least eight years. Some 25 patents were discovered by a researcher for the Wireless Consumer Alliance in the United Kingdom by Carl Hilliard. The wording in the patents speaks to "suggestions" of health risks and that there is no contradiction of their public pronouncements of safety while nailing down the intellectual property rights to solve a problem they deny exists.

"Public exposure to electromagnetic radiation (radiofrequency and microwave) is growing exponentially worldwide with the introduction and use of cordless phones, cellular phones, pagers and antennas in communities designed to transmit their RF signals. The virtual revolution in science taking place now is based on a growing recognition that non-thermal or low intensity RF exposure can be detected in living tissues and result in well defined bioeffects. Bioeffects that are reported to result from RF exposure include changes in cell membrane function, metabolism, cellular signal communication, activation of proto-oncogenes, and cell death. Resulting effects which are reported in the scientific literature include DNA breaks and chromosome aberrations, increased free radical production, cell stress and premature aging, changes in cell membrane function including memory loss, learning impairment, headaches and fatigue, sleep disorders, neurodegenerative conditions, reductions in melatonin secretion, and cancer. The United States has a de facto policy of 'post-sales surveillance' with respect to cell phones. That means cell phones can be sold to the public, and only after years of use will there be

101 Nic Fleming & Ian Cobain, "Mobile Firms Patent Cancer Shields," The London Times, June 11,2001, http://www.thetimes.co.uk EPI3395

studies to characterize what health consequences, if any, have arisen as a result."102

Some scientists are even warning that constant cell phone use causes premature aging. "Low level radiation from the phone 'heats up' body cells, damaging skin and making the user look lined and haggard. The study by Nottingham University's School of Biological Sciences is the latest research to raise concerns about the effect of mobile phones on health. Dr. David De Pomerai, who is in charge of the research team, said: 'Gradually, cells don't work properly, so the life process becomes less efficient.' Dr. De Pomerai said that heavy mobile phone users were just like heavy smokers who constantly inhaled cell-damaging toxins without allowing the body time to repair the harm."103

The Effect on Children

While some manufacturers target children for cell phone sales, experts point out that "cell phone radiation penetrates the skulls and brains of kids more deeply than adults, and that this radiation might cause tumors or otherwise affect a developing brain. Several brands of cell phones exceed the radiation limits specified in FCC guidelines, ABC News show 20/20 reported. Dr. Ross Adey, a widely published RF researcher stated that 'Children categorically should not, be encouraged or allowed to use' cell phones."104

"Overall, the available data on EMF and cancer (especially leukemia, brain and breast cancer) are too inconsistent to establish a cause-and-effect relationship, but there is enough evidence of association to raise concern. As a matter of fact, epidemiology has seen a large number of examples where health hazards were initially described with unconvincing and sometimes inadequate experiments which demonstrated a weak association

102 Sage, Cindy. Sage Associates, Santa Barbara, CA. Letter to the Clerk of the Transport and the Environment Committee, The Scottish Parliament. EPI1837

103 *Daily Mail*. "Using a mobile phone makes you age faster." Oct. 18, 1999. EPI1814

104 Whittelsey, Frances. "Cell Phones and Kids: A Bad Call?" *vote.com*, 1999. EPI1791

with a given environmental influence. Such associations were found between cholera and drinking water containing fecal contaminants, between smoking and lung cancer or between exposure to vinyl chloride and certain forms of liver cancer. All these associations were highly questioned in the past and are now well recognized."[105] The situation has developed where the existing standards of safety do not apply and yet industries with billions of dollars at risk continue to deny the problems or attempt to limit their liability by keeping the debate infused with rhetoric as they busily seek and file patents to "save the day" when the "truth" emerges from their ashes of denial – again the betrayal of science, this time for money at the expense of the public. EMF risks and the research surrounding the risks can be quantified by "applying the laws of physics to living systems as open systems" which interact with everything around and passing through them. Those words still echo through my mind from 1978 when Dr. Reijo Mäkala first spoke them to me. Dr. Mäkala has passed on yet his ideas remain decades ahead of the current level of scientific knowledge embraced by the mainstream of science. Now a few decades later the day seems to be nearing when these ideas will be widely held. Today the evidence is overwhelming and expanding.

Current Research On Cell Phones Confirms Earlier Studies of Risk

Though 110 million Americans were projected to use cell phones by the end of 2001[106], Europeans began widespread use of them much earlier with many now reporting side effects from their use. "Monica Sandstrom, of the Swedish National Institute for Working Life, unveiled data from her agency's survey of cell phone users – 5,000 in Norway and 12,000 in Sweden. 'One quarter of the Norwegian users, she noted, feel warmth on or behind the ear when they use their phones....20 percent also linked frequent headaches and recurring fatigue to cell-phone use. At least one of the symptoms noted, which include dizziness, concentration difficulties, memory loss, and a burning sensation,

105 Verschaeve, L. "Can non ionizing radiation induce cancer?" *The Cancer Journal*, Vol. 8, No. 5. EPI1797

106 General Accounting Office, "Telecommunication - Research and Regulatory Efforts on Mobile Phone Health Issues." GAO-01-545, May 2001 Report to Congressional Requesters, United States Government. EPI3348

showed up in 47 percent of people who reported using these wireless devices an hour or more daily.' W. Ross Adey of the University of California, speculates that increased enzyme activity, which can foster certain cancers, 'may offer an explanation' of tumors that he and his colleagues have observed in rats exposed to RF energy for long periods."[107] The most important factor consistently surfacing throughout the world, whether in China, Russia, United States or in numerous European centers of research, was that the results were the same and caution was being expressed.

"On March 9, the China Consumers Association (CCA) issued a 'worrisome' warning about Chinese cell phones' electromagnetic radiation and how this might affect phone users, the March 10 Yangcheng Wanbao reported. According to the CCA, tests have found that some cell phones' radiation was as high as 10,000 microwatts per square centimeter (1,550 mw per square inch)." The newspaper noted a study by China's Northern Communications University which said that half of cell phone's radiation is absorbed by the human body and another quarter by the brain.[108]

"Experts studying mobile phones are waiting to investigate new research from Poland which reportedly establishes a link between the devices and cancer. *The Sunday Mirror* newspaper said the 20-year study of servicemen had established 'the strongest link yet', showing a high cancer death rate among soldiers exposed to microwave radiation, 'the same as that emitted by the phones.'"[109]

"Using a mobile phone could drastically reduce your sex drive, new research shows....Researchers tested rats and mice using microwave radiation at lower levels similar to those emitted by mobile phones. Scientists discovered that exposed rats had far less testosterone in their blood stream than those which remained unexposed. The higher the dose of radiation, the less testosterone

107 Raloff, J. "Researchers Probe Cell-Phone Effects." *Science News,* Feb. 12, 2000. EPI1872

108 *Consumidor.* "Consumer Group Says China Cell Radiation Levels Unsafe." March 16, 2000. EPI1873

109 *Reuters.* "Mobile Phones Report Claims 'Strongest Link Yet' To Cancer." March 27, 2000. EPI1870

was released by the body's glands, resulting in diminished sexual activity." The test results are being studied in Britain, where scientists are conducting similar research.110 The other important factor to keep in mind is that in the larger context of how living things interact with various kinds of energy sources is that there are effects from both subtle and high energy sources. The effect of sound and light at very low concentrations allows us to sort out with our eyes and ears the radiation emitted from many sources. What allows us to see color differences between objects is a very slight variation in the energy absorbed by an object and that portion reflected to the eye. The eye as an electromagnetic receiver "sees" the signal which is decoded by the brain. These natural energy interactions are what will be created in bio-electric circuits in the future linking mankind inseparably from our machines.

"Current safety guidelines for cell phones assume no harmful effects, as long as the microwave radiation they emit does not cause heating of body tissue. Exposure limits are intended to protect us only from excessive temperatures caused by absorption of energy, a known danger linked to the intensity of radio-frequency microwaves." But living cells respond in non-thermal ways to the fields produced by cell phones, and at intensities below the established safety threshold.111 These energy levels are below the ionizing level. "Ionizing radiation is a well-established risk factor for brain tumors. During recent years, microwave exposure from the use of cellular telephones has been discussed as a risk factor." A case-control study was undertaken, with exposure assessed by questionnaires. It was determined that "Exposure to ionizing radiation, work in laboratories, and work in the chemical industry increased the risk of brain tumors. Use of a cellular telephone was associated with an increased risk in the anatomic area with highest exposure."112 These and other energy exposures are having significant effects on health.

"In addition to extremely-low-frequency (ELF) electric power fields, many millions of mobile phone users worldwide are

110 *Sunday Mirror.* "Beware - Using A Mobile Can Ruin Your Sex Life." April 16, 2000. EPI1871

111 MacArthur, John. "The Cell Phone Chronicles." *brain.com*, April 25, 2000. EPI1845

112 Hardell et al. "Case-Control Study on Radiology Work, Medical X-ray Investigations, and Use of Cellular Telephones as Risk Factors for Brain Tumors."*medscape.com*, May 4, 2000. EPI1893

now also exposed daily to radiofrequency fields under near-field conditions. We may expect that these newly evolved behavioral patterns will be lifelong, with intermittent exposures at the phone user's head making yet one more contribution to an already complex daily EMF exposure arising in an aggregate of multiple and disparate sources."[113]

The cell phone industry continues to downplay the risk and call for more research. Meanwhile we understand the delays while waiting for the stringent proofs required to change the foundations of the life sciences which will occur when the impact of low intensity energy is understood. In the meantime waiting for the proof in after-the-fact studies does not reassure the public. The precautionary principle is a good one for an age where technology is doubled every few months and the impact of that technology may not be known for years after. We need to open the doors in this area and find ways to reduce risk and exposures to EMFs, particularly those created by home remote and cell phones.

Independent Research Funded by Industry
Dr. Carlo

"Dr. George Carlo is Chairman of the Carlo Institute. He is a Fellow of the American College of Epidemiology, and is a specialist in assessing and managing risks to public health. His work has included studies addressing risks from the environment and consumer products, as well as the safety and efficacy of pharmaceuticals and medical devices. Dr. Carlo serves on the faculty of The George Washington University School of Medicine. Dr. Carlo has served in diverse scientific advisory capacities, including membership on the US Congress Office of Technology Assessment Agent Orange Advisory Panel, the chairmanship of Wireless Technology Research, LLC, and director of the Breast Implant Public Health Project, LLC."[114] This would be the person behind one of the most important cell phone studies of the last century and the precursor to the storm.

113 Adey, Dr. W. Ross. "Cell And Molecular Biology Associated With Radiation Fields Of Mobile Telephones." Department of Biochemistry, University of California. EPI1799

114 *electric-words.com.* "Dr. George L. Carlo et. al. and the fiasco called Wireless Technology Research." EPI1858

The industry has been involved in attempting to influence the research and has been required to pay for independent research. The companies involved have attempted to control the data flow to the public as information has become available. As far back as 1996 the issues began to surface with the following report. "Motorola, Inc. planned two years ago how to collaborate with the Cellular Telecommunications Industry Association and Wireless Technology Research L.L.C. to downplay potentially damaging scientific findings on possible health risks from portable telephones, according to a Dec. 1994 internal Motorola memo."[115] The company the industry sought to collaborate with was the firm which eventually used over $27,000,000 industry dollars to research the risks of cell phones. In the body of that research several issues emerged creating additional studies.

The industry has continued to place a premium on information and continues to monitor what is developing in public debate with an eye to framing that debate to their advantage. "The US wireless industry, responding to the global proliferation of media coverage of mobile phone health concerns and to Internet-savvy activists, is leading an effort to create a worldwide information-sharing network to counter negative publicity. The Wireless Industry Global Information Network, or WIN, held its first meeting Dec. 10 [1998] in London."[116] This organization was set up interestingly enough in advance of the initial report of findings they had paid to research and were now fearful of. The public relations plans began to unfold through a coordinated industry effort to control the damage to the industry likely to result from the report.

The story began to break. The head of the industry sponsored research issued his report of findings. Dr. Carlo took a conservative approach to his release of findings but his concerns were clear – precaution might be required. "There may be a correlation between cell phone use and cancer, according to the director of the program. 'The data, while 'important' only suggest that more research is necessary,' said George Carlo, chairman of the industry-funded Wireless Technology Research

115 Silva, Jeffrey. "Motorola Memo Raises Questions About WTR Research." *RCR*, March 3, 1997. EPI1820

116 Silva, Jeffrey. "Industry launches global effort to counter cancer claims." *RCR News*, Jan. 25, 1999. EPI1822

group. 'We're now in a gray area that we've never been in before with this. When we're in a gray area, the best thing to do is let the public know about the findings so that they can make their own judgment,' he said.' WTR was formed by industry in 1993 and funded with $25 million to conduct independent studies. The studies put animal cells through 46 tests for cancer-inducing genetic damage. The research was conducted at Stanford University and Integrated Laboratory Systems in Research Triangle Park."117 "The close of the six-year, $27 million Wireless Technology Research L.L.C. program has re-energized a public debate about whether mobile telephones cause cancer or pose other health problems to the nation's 70 million wireless subscribers. Indeed, WTR Chairman George Carlo claims new studies suggest a possible mobile phone-cancer link. While saying the results do not rise to the level of a public health problem, Carlo insists the findings demand serious attention of the federal government and wireless industry."118 The problems were instead dealt with in a manner which masked the risks rather than warn the public of the dangers. Now, some years later, while most vehemently denying the risks the industry was preparing new patents to solve the cell phone radiation emissions problems.

The industry was not happy with the results of their study. "The cellular phone industry probably didn't pay researchers US$27 million dollars hoping they'd produce bad news about the health effects of cell phones. Nonetheless, an industry-funded study has done just that. While the findings are far from conclusive. They are the first from an organization like the industry supported Wireless Technology Research. 'You would come to the [possible] conclusion that RF [radio frequencies] causes genetic damage,' [Chairman George] Carlo said. 'that is a huge surprise.'

The findings represent a need for coordinated public health action while there is more investigation into the hazards, he added. 'When you have 200 million people who are being exposed to cell phones, you can't wait around for the slow

117 Schwartz, John. "Cell Phones May Have Cancer Link." *Washington Post*, May 22, 1999. EPI1785

118 Silva, Jeffrey. "Controversy follows WTR to the end." June 4, 1999. EPI1821

scientific process to work.'"119 Dr. Carlo's initial reports were framed in the standard conservative approach taken in finding the facts which science can then demonstrate. His research indicated serious concerns based on the evidence but was not conclusive. He felt that industry should pay attention and pursue the research. "In an astonishing attack on the industry for which he once acted as a spokesman, he accused firms of not taking safety seriously. 'The companies are now spending millions trying to discredit me because, basically, they didn't like what I told them', he revealed to *The Express* last night. 'I feel angry and let down.' After presenting its results to the phone companies in February, he claims they failed to take 'the appropriate steps to protect consumers'. Dr. Carlo, a leading public health scientist based in Washington, said: They have shown total disregard for mobile phone users.'"120 Dr. Carlo did not stop there. He went on to publish a book for lay people on the subject which was released in January 2001.

The project director did get the information to the right people in the hope that the public could be protected by the application of precaution for the consumer. "Dr. George Carlo, in his capacity as director of Wireless Technology Research, wrote a letter to the CEO of AT&T which has serious legal implications for mobile phone manufacturers who have claimed that there is no evidence for adverse health effects from mobile phone use. With the letter widely circulated in the industry, making that claim now could possibly expose them to litigation in much the same way as what happened to the tobacco industry, where it was shown that industry assurances of no evidence of hazards from smoking was a complete fabrication."121 The difference between the tobacco industry litigation and the situation with cell phones is that the industry is regulated by standards of safety established by the federal government. In fact, the US Supreme Court let stand a lower court ruling that shielded Motorola and other companies from state law claims with respect to cell phone safety. A suit filed by Frank Schiffner had asserted that Motorola did not provide

119 Oakes, Chris. "Cell Study: Hazards Are Real." *Wired Magazine*, June 21, 1999. EPI1805

120 Gallagher, Ian et al. "Mobile Phones Cover-UP." *The Express* (UK), Oct. 16, 1999. EPI1808

121 Maisch, Don. "A Letter Bomb For The Mobile Phone Industry?" EMFacts Consultancy, Oct. 19, 1999. EPI1806

information about the health risks or incorporate design modifications in these phones so as to minimize risks to users. 122

Quoting from "Dr. George Carlo's letter to Mr. C. Michael Armstrong, Chairman of AT&T Corporation the potential risks were presented:

> '* The rate of death from brain cancer among handheld phone users was higher than the rate of brain cancer death among those who used non-handheld phones that were away from their head;
>
> * The risk of acoustic neuroma, a benign tumor of the auditory nerve that is well in the range of the radiation coming from a phone's antenna, was fifty percent higher in people who reported using cell phones for six years or more, moreover, that relationship between the amount of cell phone use and this tumor appeared to follow a dose-response curve;
>
> * The risk of rare neuro epithelial tumors on the outside of the brain was more than doubled, a statistically significant risk increase, in cell phone users as compared to people who did not use cell phones;
>
> * There appeared to be some correlation between brain tumors occurring on the right side of the head and the use of the phone on the right side of the head;
>
> * Laboratory studies looking at the ability of radiation from a phone's antenna to cause functional genetic damage were definitely positive, and were following a dose-response relationship.
>
> I also indicated that while our overall study of brain cancer occurrence did not show a

122 *Chicago Sun Times,* "Phone Makers Not Liable", March 23, 1999 EPI____

correlation with cell phone use, the vast majority of the tumors that were studied, were well out of range of the radiation that one would expect from a cell phone's antenna. Because of that distance, the finding of no effect was questionable.

Today I sit here extremely frustrated and concerned that appropriate steps have not been taken by the wireless industry to protect consumers during this time of uncertainty about safety.

I am concerned that the wireless industry is missing a valuable opportunity by dealing with these public health concerns through politics, creating illusions that more research over the next several years helps consumers today, and false claims that regulatory compliance means safety. The better choice by the wireless industry would be to implement measured steps aimed at true consumer protection.

The most important measures of consumer protection are missing: complete and honest factual information to allow informed judgment by consumers about assumption of risk; the direct tracking and monitoring of what happens to consumers who use wireless phones; and, the monitoring of changes in the technology that could impact health."123

On the program ABC 20/20™ Dr. Carlo continued expressing his concern and dismay in the way he was handled by the industry. "You cannot guarantee that cell phones are safe. That's absolutely true, but that has always been true. [Brian] Ross: ...The cell phone transmits a microwave signal from an antenna to a base station or tower, often miles away. The farther from the tower, or if the phone is inside a building or a car, the more power this phone is told by the tower to send out to make or keep the connection. Depending on how close the cell phone

123 Carlo, George L. Letter to Mr. C. Michael Armstrong, Chairman and Chief Executive Officer, AT & T Corporation. EPI1807

antenna is, as much as 60 percent of the microwave radiation is absorbed by and actually penetrates the area around the head, some reaching an inch to an inch and a half into the brain."124

On the same day Dr. Carlo was quoted by ABC News as saying, "'The industry had come out and said that there were thousands of studies that proved that wireless phones are safe, and the fact was that there were no studies that were directly relevant,' says Dr. George Carlo. 'We've moved into an area where we now have some direct evidence of possible harm from cellular phones.' The $200-billion-a-year cell phone industry maintains the devices are safe."125

The FDA as a result of this research and others finally announced a study of their own. "Federal safety regulators are investigating whether microwave radiation from cell phones causes cancer or other diseases. The investigation was triggered by two industry-sponsored studies that the Food and Drug Administration said require additional research. The question of cell-phone safety recently led Metrocall of Alexandria, Va., the nation's third largest pager company and a major seller of AT&T cellular phones, to warn its sales staff that parents buying for a child or young adult should consider a pager instead of a cell phone 'due to potential health risks."126 These risks to children continue to be confirmed by others who have independently reached the same conclusions.127

Liability and Possible Claims

In the initial days of the controversy regarding cell phones the industry developed a huge public relations effort in the face of lawsuits and adverse press reports impacting the industry. Paul

124 20/20 ABC TV. "Worried About Your Wireless?" Oct. 20, 1999. Unedited transcript. EPI1828

125 Ross, Brian. "Wireless Worries?" *abcnews.com*, Oct. 20, 1999. EPI1790

126 Rosenberg et al. "Cell-phone health risks need to be studied, FDA says." *Seattle Post-Intelligencer*. April 1, 2000. EPI1827

127 Reuters Limited, "Scientist Raises New Mobile Phone Fears," November 25, 2000, http://dailnews.yahoo.com/htx/nm/20001125/ts/health_mobilephones_dc_1.html EPI2810

Staiano, President of Motorola General Systems stated, "Forty years of research and more than ten thousand studies have proved that cellular phones are safe."128 This quote, from the industry, was an incredible exaggeration of the research as it related to cell phone risks. "Since then, however, the industry has largely put forth studies that looked at the effects of radio waves outside the cellular frequency, or at exposure levels that are different from those experienced by cellular phone users."

"'The industry hasn't told the public the full story about how there has been very little research on biological effects at low level exposures, similar to those of handheld phones,' says Louis Slesin, editor of *Microwave News,* a New York newsletter and a frequent critic of the industry's handling of the safety issue."129 Very limited information has been available to the public about the risks of cell phones or various electromagnetic fields outside of some obscure research in academic circles. The fact is that increasing evidence has been mounting and the true risks of these energy fields are becoming well known.

The possibility of another tobacco-type of health scandal was perhaps in the offing when a closed Congressional hearing was held to develop regulations and recommend further studies of electromagnetic field (EMF) health effects. They suggested moderation in phone use until more is known while an FDA paper, dated Feb. 4, 1992, suggested: '...those who spend long periods of time on their hand-held cellular phones could consider holding lengthy conversations on conventional phones and reserving the hand-held cellular models for shorter conversat-ions...'"130 Many studies have been sponsored by industry, academic institutions, government laboratories and by military research organizations into the effects of low levels of electromagnetic radiation. The constant problem in the debate of risks is the limited knowledge about the fact that very specific fields interacting with our bodies can in fact cause a significant effect on

128 Goldberg, Robert B. "The Cellular Phone Controversy: Real or Contrived?" *EMF Health Report,* Vol. 1, No. 1, 1993. EPI1793

129 Keller, John J. "Are They Safe?" *Wall Street Journal,* Feb. 11, 1994. EPI1878

130 "Nominations from FDA's Center from Device and Radiological Health: Radio Frequency Radiation Emissions of Wireless Communication Devices" (CDRH). Feb. 8, 2000. EPI1874

our health. These effects vary throughout populations with some effected to a greater degree than others. This is related to our physical and biochemical differences. The research which is being conducted by the industry is ignoring much of what has already appeared in the literature regarding risk factors. Moreover the base of research is ignoring the underlying disconnect between biological science and physics as it applies to living systems. The old school places the emphasis on the chemical model for accounting for and creating reactions in the human body whereas the new school of thought drops below this level to the underlying electromagnetic exchanges which occur in advance of chemical reactions. The interactions do not require the intensity of energy interactions once thought to regulate and define what is "safe."

The FDA concluded in a February 8, 2000 report that, "There is currently insufficient scientific basis for concluding that wireless communication technologies are safe or that they pose a risk to millions of users. A significant research effort, including well planned animal experiments, is needed to provide the basis to assess the risk to human health of wireless communications devices."[131]

The FDA has begun a three to five year study to look at some of these effects. This comes at the conclusion of the industry sponsored Carlo study which, together with other recent studies, shows increasing risk to human health related to cell phone emissions.

Congress passed the Telecommunications Act of 1996, P.L. 101-104, 110 Stat. 56(1996). "Section 704 of the act amends the Communications Act by providing federal preemption of state and local regulation of personal wireless service facilities on the basis of RF environmental effects."[132] In other words states and local communities may not adopt more stringent protections if the federal regulatory authorities fail to protect the public. This limits the rights of states or local governments and essentially leaves any risk assessment and solution to the federal level regulatory authorities. This issue has been confirmed by the

131 "Nominations from FDA's Center from Device and Radiological Health: Radio Frequency Radiation Emissions of Wireless Communication Devices (CDRH). Feb. 8, 2000. EPI1874

132 Federal Communications Commission. "Radiofrequency FAQs Page." Office of Engineering and Technology. June 1, 1998. EPI2062

Supreme Court in limiting the liability of companies133 by deferring to the regulations as the guide for industry while giving the only authority to federal agencies already reporting a lack of capacity in recruiting personnel in the necessary areas.134

The FDA approach and the reluctance of the United States government to move on this issue is directly related to lobby efforts, public relations gimmicks and the manipulation of the facts behind what is a major concern to many. At present the evidence is causing some to follow the "precautionary principle" in dealing with the potential adverse health consequences of cell phones and other sources of radio frequency radiation. Other governments were taking a different approach. "The [Australian] Senate late yesterday agreed to a Senate inquiry into electromagnetic emissions (EME), particularly from mobile phones. Senator Allison said the inquiry is necessary because of the Federal Government's ongoing failure to ensure that public health issues are properly considered in standard setting for mobile phone emissions. The Minister for Communications and the industry refuse to acknowledge what most Australians know intuitively; that it is not just the heat from mobile phones that is a potential health risk."135

Studies to determine if there is a cancer-cell phone radio frequency (RF) EMF link are ongoing and others are planned. "A study funded by McCaw Cellular Communications will determine the amount of RF EMF given off by cellular phones and its pattern of absorption in the human head and brain."136 This study was eventually completed leading to the earlier cited $27,000,000 study. The Carlo study, as an industry sponsored research effort, indicated serious concerns for the industry.

The risks associated with cell phones are being considered too risky even by the biggest risk takers in the insurance industry. "Concern about the safety of mobile phones has prompted a

133 "Phone Makers Not Liable," Chicago Sun Times, March 23, 1999.

134 General Accounting Office, "Telecommunication - Research and Regulatory Efforts on Mobile Phone Health Issues." GAO-01-545, May 2001 Report to Congressional Requesters, United States Government. EPI3348

135 Allison, Senator Lyn. "Democrats Deliver Senate Inquiry On Mobile Phones." Australian Democrats Spokeperson on Telecommunications, Dec. 9, 1999. EPI1885

136 Goldberg, Robert B. "The Cellular Phone Controversy: Real or Contrived?" *EMF Health Report*, Vol. 1, No. 1, 1993. EPI1793

leading Lloyd's underwriter to refuse to insure phone manufacturers against the risk of damage to users' health...fears that mobile phones will be linked to illnesses such as cancer and Alzheimers have prompted John Fenn, of underwriting group Sterling, to refuse to cover manufacturers against the risk of being sued if mobiles turn out to cause long-term damage."137 Risk management and the kinds of legal concerns arising out of the tobacco law suits has turned insurers of product liability claims on their heads. Insurance underwriters investigate risk through the review of information available to them. The level of evidence they need, to move in the direction of safety is lower than the absolute proofs of science. Risk management is based on how information starts to form and when the risks are beyond the prudence of those who take the risks of insurance, risks are avoided. Who is right? When is the public's risk placed ahead of insurance risks? Underwriters are looking at the risk "Should it become clear that the digital pulsed modulation signal does have adverse effects – which may act as triggers to adverse health conditions – then manufacturers could face massive legal claims for failing to provide any or adequate health warnings to mobile phone users. Lloyds of London has, I understand, refused to issue product liability cover for manufacturers and sellers on mobiles..."138 Employers may also be liable according to legal and other opinions.139 "Employers are usually required to provide a safe system of work. A number of employers expect their employees to carry out their duties and responsibilities using mobile phones for hours at a time. It could well turn out to be a non-safe system of work for which substantial damages may be awarded as a result of adverse health conditions. A number of cases have already been settled out of court but again are subject to confidentiality clauses."140

137 Ryle, Sarah. "Insurers balk at risks of phones." The London Observer, April 11, 1999. EPI1796

138 Meyer, Alan. Senior partner: Halsey Meyer Higgins, Solicitors, London. "Mobile Phones and Mobile Networks: Potential Litigation Or Law Suits." EPI1850

139 Bob Brewin & Jennifer DiSabatino, *Computerworld*, "CIOs Warned of Cell Phone Risks - Corporate Liability Issue Researcher Says", July 31, 2000 EPI2197

140 Meyer, Alan. Senior partner: Halsey Meyer Higgins, Solicitors, London. "Mobile Phones and Mobile Networks: Potential Litigation Or Law Suits." EPI1850

Companies recognizing potential third party litigation have also been attempting to reduce their risk. Reasonable technological advances which could decrease risk are being put forward by employers who require cell phone use in the course of employee work. The risk of future litigation if the precaution is not considered increases. "Europe's third largest manufacturer of electrical appliances, Merloni Elettrodomestici SpA, has decided to supply its employees with dual-band cell phones capable of operating with a microphone and headphones for safety reasons. The decision follows a major press campaign in Italy on the dangers of electromagnetic waves. [CEO Francesco] Caio is very sensitive to the problems of health and the environment and some of our employees had begun to express doubts and worries."141 The other concern is that perhaps other risks are created in the solutions. As is described in the research, although removal of the cell phone from the head is helpful to the head it can still expose the body to the effects of its radiation. Safety issues are an increasing concern but information has become fragmented. The issues of safety as discussed elsewhere in this text begin to bring the issue together from several points of view.

Base-stations or cell phone towers may also pose risks. "The installation of base stations for mobile telephone systems has been delayed or has met opposition from the public because of concerns that the RF emissions from these base stations might cause cancer in children. In the United States, for example, 85% of the total number of base stations needed have yet to be constructed.142 The increase in these systems and their interaction with other energy fields in our homes, cars and work places may in fact be significantly increasing health risks. The issues surrounding the placement of cell towers have been of concern in Europe where some studies have been conducted. In the United States locating cell towers on private land has become the norm based on individual negotiations with property owners. Even churches are being targeted as site locations where the transmission tower is located in the steeple in exchange for an initial fee and annual payments. 143 Towers are also being hidden in our

141 Willan, Philip. "Cell-phone safety at issue in Italy." *IDG News Service*, May 20, 1999. EPI1798

142 World Health Organization. "Electromagnetic Fields And Public Health." Fact Sheet N181. May 1998. EPI1787

143 Gram, David, *Anchorage Daily News*, Associated Press, "Cellphone Companies Woo Churches as Antenna Sites", January 20, 2001 EPI3008

communities using camouflage structures which appear to look like trees so that their appearance throughout the country might blend into communities more efficiently.144

International organizations are also looking at the risks because of increasing public concern, scientific evidence and industry concerns. "In May 1996, in response to growing public health concerns in many member states over possible health effects from exposure to an ever-increasing number and diversity of EMF sources, the World Health Organization (WHO) launched an international project to assess health and environmental effects of exposure to electric and magnetic fields, which became known as the International EMF Project."145 Other studies are already producing the evidence of biological effects. "Finally there was recently a study funded by the Bavarian State Government in Germany following reported adverse health effects in dairy cattle only after a Telecoms Mast had been erected. It was discovered after a period of time that the cause of the significant drop in the yield of that herd of cattle and Extraordinary Behavior Disorders in some of the cows related to the microwave transmissions from that mast. When the cattle were moved away from its vicinity, after a period the milk yield and the behavior of that herd was restored to normal."146

The research continues and the health effects mount. With over 1.3 billion people projected to be using these devices in the year 2005 the risks must be understood and addressed. Perhaps we will see the litigation of the 21st century overtake the incredible tobacco settlements as the record holder for "damage by industry when its head's in the sand."

Choosing on the Side of Safety

"On October 31, 1996, the US National Academy of Sciences, National Research Council (NAS/NRC) issued a review of the EMF literature: *Possible Health Effects of Exposure to Residential Electric and Magnetic Fields.* The conclusions of this report are that '*there is no* **conclusive and consistent** *evidence*

144 Valmont Microflect, Valmont Industries, Camouflage Structures, 1997 http://www.comtowers-poles.com/camo.htm EPI2609

77 World Health Organization. "Electromagnetic Fields And Public Health." Fact Sheet N181. May 1998. EPI1787

146 Halsey Meyer Higgins, Solicitors, London. "Mobile Phones - Mobile Networks - Safety." Sept. 10, 1995. EPI1849

showing that exposure to residential electric and magnetic fields produces cancer, adverse neurobehavioral effects, or reproductive and developmental defects'. Of significant importance are the words,'conclusive and consistent'. Like the more familiar phrase in law, 'beyond reasonable doubt', 'conclusive and consistent' implies a certain standard of evidence that warrants more serious action. Using that type of reasoning, the NRC Committee concluded that research results do not show that EMF exposure at a residential environmental level causes adverse health effects."147

"The FDA advises persons concerned about exposure to cell phone radiation to take some simple steps to avoid exposure. Those persons who spend long periods of time on their hand-held mobile phones could consider holding lengthy conversations on conventional phones and reserving the hand-held models for shorter conversations. People who must conduct extended conversations in their cars every day could switch to a type of mobile phone that places more distance between their bodies and the source of RF, since the exposure level drops off dramatically with distance."148 How cell phones might effect our health is compelling people to take heed of the warnings and find ways to reduce exposure without giving up the device. Some have resorted to earpieces and belt level phones. This may in fact be even worse than head exposure because of the way in which the phone then operates. More power is required and exposure to softer tissue allows more energy to transfer into the body.

A European report reads as follows: "The 'precautionary principle' is recognized by European Governments in the Maastricht Treaty and forms the basis of both EU and UK regulation in this area. Under a strict application, it would not be possible to balance the risks of harm with the benefits of technological advances, since even a small degree of uncertainty or a suspicion of possible harm, no matter how ill-judged, would be enough to prohibit the introduction of a new technology. This interpretation is not, however, sustainable; it would preclude the application of almost any significant development as almost all innovations may have hidden or unknown risks. In practice,

147 Maisch et al. "Powerline Frequency Electromagnetic Fields and Human Health - Is it the time to end further research?" March 1998. EPI1819

148 FDA. "Consumer Update on Mobile Phones." Center for Devices and Radiological Health. Oct. 20, 1999. EPI1801

therefore, applying the precautionary principle means measures must be taken to minimize known risks and alertness to the emergence of unknown risks must be maintained.[149]"

The report continues in discussing the use of cell phones in vehicles. "Cars and other vehicles screen the microwave emissions from the mobile phone when in use and so act as a Faraday cage. GSM phones compensate for this by increasing the power output resulting in greater microwave absorption in the user.[150]" In other words because the signal is trapped in the car frame it requires more energy to send the signal to the nearest cell phone tower.

Hands Free Kits

The issue of safety is addressed on several fronts in the case of "hands free kits." Many users of these devices believe that by using these devices they will be safer from the radiation emitted from the phone. The problem is that they do not protect the user in the way expected. In some legal cases pending before courts in four states, attorneys are seeking a solution which includes reimbursement, or free issuance of hands free kits, in order to reduce radiation. The misconception of the public, legal experts[151] and others that these devices offer safety from radiation is incorrect and again demonstrates the need for better developed consumer information.

Another area where hands free kits offer some level of increased safety has to do with keeping our hands on the streering wheel of the automobile rather than holding a phone. In a highly controversial move the New York legislature addressed the issue by limiting the use of cell phones in automobiles to hands free devices only.[152] This issue was pursued by a New York Assem-

149 House of Commons, Great Britain. Third Report, The Science and Technology Committee. "Scientific Advisory System: Mobile Phones And Health, Sept. 22, 1999. EPI1895

150 Ibid.

151 CNN, "Makers of Cellphones Hit with Class-action Suits", April 19, 2001, http://www.rfsafe.com/cnn_041901.htm

152 Michaud, Chris, Reuters Limited, "New York Bans Drivers Using Hand-held Cellphones", June 28, 2001,

blyman, Felix Ortiz, who began following the issue over five years ago pressing for a change in the law in the interest of public safety. He encountered significant resistance from the industry which was overshadowed by the pleas of parents who lost children in car accidents related to cell phone use while operating a vehicle.

Hands free kits are also discussed revealing the hidden risks. "Currently, the cellular industry are encouraging the use of hands free kits, but cite their only advantage as being to offer greater freedom of use to the user, nothing else. The fact is they know the real reason users are buying them is because they think these kits protect them from radiation exposure. Recent tests have shown that whilst exposure to the head is reduced by around 70 percent, all that is happening is the radiation is being transferred to another part of the body which is potentially more vulnerable because it does not have the thickness of the skull to protect itself – the waist or chest areas."[153] "Commenting on the news in the British consumer magazine *Which?*, "theoretical physicist Dr. Zvi Weinberg said it's probable that earpieces serve as antennae that direct more electromagnetic radiation into the ears. However, he said, phone models may differ in the degree to which their internal wires conduct electricity, and said he planned to calculate the various mechanisms involved during the next two weeks."[154] "It turns out that 'hands-free' cell phones may not save you from the Grim Reaper after all. Alarming claims surfaced last week in a research publication in the U.K. that not only are many hands-free devices useless in protecting wireless phone users from radiation that might cause tumors, these products may actually raise the amount of radiation being directed into the head by three times." The report, by Antonia Chitty, appeared in *Which?* magazine, a 700,000-subscriber consumer report which does not accept advertising. The test results of the study, according to *Which?*, showed that the earplugs in the hands-free kit acted as aerials and channeled more radiation into the ear model than standard cell phones did. The earphones channel three times the

153 House of Commons, Great Britain. Third Report, The Science and Technology Committee. "Scientific Advisory System: Mobile Phones And Health." Sept. 22, 1999. EPI1895

154 *Jerusalem Post*. "Experts Debate Safety Of Earpieces For Cell Phone." April 6, 2000. EPI1868

dose of radiation into the ear than a regular cellular phone does. 155, 156

Using a mobile phone clipped to your waist results in a hotspot of radiation being pumped into the liver and kidneys. "There is concern that they may intensify radiation exposure to the ear canal. Using a hands-free kit and making a call with a mobile phone clipped to your belt also means the phone will generally be working at a higher power level. That's because it is generally harder to transmit from waist-height than head height. But there's a lot of body tissue in that area which has good conductivity and absorbs radiation more quickly than the head." People think hands-free kits are safer, so tend to spend more time on the phone. The phone works harder to pick up a signal if it is down by the waist, where more radiation is absorbed than by the head."157

In the process of looking for solutions to improve the hands free systems a simple idea was put forward by the U.K. government's Independent Expert Group on Mobile Phones. The energy that was transferred from the phone into the ear could be reduced by fitting a small ring made of an iron-based compound (ferrite) to the headset. "The ferrite choke acts as a high impedance to the wave and reflects it back down the cable."158

Non-thermal Verses Thermal Effects

Non-thermal verses thermal effects are also being considered by the Europeans in trying to establish increased margins of safety. "The NRPB and industry's position that mobiles are safe, is based on the facts that all handsets comply with current recommended limits, which are based on thermal considerations only. As you had already probably been made aware, the literature is full of published papers showing damage

155 McGinity, Meg. "Yacking Yourself To Death?" *zdnet.com,* April 10, 2000. EPI1867

156 CNN, "U.K. Consumer Group: Hands-free Phone Kits Boost Radiation Exposure", November 2, 2000, http:/www.cnn.com/2000/TECH/computing/11/02/london.phone/index.html ERI2969

157 *The Sunday Mirror.* "Cell Phone On Your Belt Brings Radiation To Liver And Kidneys." July 10, 1999. EPI1786

158 Marks, Paul, *New Scientist,* "Give us a Ring", November 11, 2000. http://www.newscientist.com/nsplus/insight/phones/giveusaring.html EPI2962

and biological effects at power levels which were set deliberately well below thermal thresholds and therefore by definition could not have been caused by thermal damage. Even if we assume the thermal only argument to be correct, there are circumstances which the group should be aware of, where exposure exceeds even the thermal limits. In another study it was determined that people could be affected by very weak fields within currently defined "safety" limits with one study suggesting that even a cell phone on standby could emit enough energy to create changes within the cells. 159

Mobile users who wear metal rimmed glasses are intensifying the exposure to their eyes by 20 percent and into the head by 6.3 percent.

Using a mobile in a vehicle can accelerate radiation levels by up to tenfold due to resonance effect."160 These risks associated with remote telephone use cannot be ignored. The maintenance of the official position that we are waiting "for the scientific proof" cannot continue without corresponding increases in safety considerations rather than the current direction of increasing exposures and a lack of protection.

"Intelligence documents show that Western governments have know about Soviet experiments using mobile phone-type radiation to cause brain damage for more than 20 years. 'The uncensored documents reveal that Soviet military scientists had successfully used microwaves of the type used by mobile phones to weaken the blood brain barrier. According to Dr. Louis Slesin...US Army scientists had succeeded in duplicating the Soviet experiments by 1977 – eight years before mobile phones became generally available in Britain.'"161 This work was done as a result of microwave bombardments of the United States Embassy in Moscow as well as reports about research by the Soviets. There was also the fact that at this particular time the

159 Rodger Coghill & Tamara Galonja-Coghill, "Endogenous Fields and Human Peripheral Blood Lymphocytes: A Big Breakthrough in Biology" January 31, 1999, http://www.goaegis.com/articles/coghill_013199.html EPI2067

160 House of Commons, Great Britain. Third Report, The Science and Technology Committee. "Scientific Advisory System: Mobile Phones And Health. Sept. 22, 1999. EPI1895

161 Moran, Kathy. "Soviet Proof That Mobile Phones Do Cause Brain Damage." *Daily Express,* Nov. 10, 1999. EPI1891

safety standards for exposure to radio frequency radiation in the Soviet Union was significantly more stringent than United States standards by almost 1000 times. "Russian and other East European countries' exposure standards for radio frequency and microwave radiation are much stricter than in the US or Western Europe. 'An attempt was made to resolve these differences at the 2nd International Conference on Problems of Electromagnetic Safety of the Human Being, held in Moscow in late 1999. Despite extensive discussions during this conference, the attempt to 'harmonize' RF/MW standards was unsuccessful with little chance of compromise in the near future. Western standard setting organizations have emphasized protection from RF/MW thermal effects...while Russia's more restrictive standard also reflects a concern over nonthermal effects and subjective symptoms.'"162

"Biological studies of enzymes and human cells exposed in vitro to radiofrequency/microwave fields have shown a number of effects which cannot be explained simply by the heating effects of radiation on which our current standards are based. These include changes in cell membrane permeability to potassium, sodium and calcium; changes in the composition or behavior of blood-forming and immunological cells; alteration of calcium ion exchange in nerve tissue; changes in the firing patterns of neurons; and changes in levels of cancer related enzymes. A study in Belgium determined that 'very close range exposure to microwaves from a cellular phone base station increased the effect of a chemical mutagen on human blood cells, leading to increased chromosomal aberrations.'"163 "High-frequency radiation such as that emitted by ultraviolet and x-rays can break molecular bonds and damage DNA. These are called ionizing radiation. Microwave radiation such as that emitted by cell phones doesn't ionize, but can heat objects in its path."164 The heat generated causes the body to begin to expend energy to cool the area and otherwise return to its equilibrium state before it was irradiated by the device.

162 Maisch, Don. "Setting radio frequency/Microwave (RF/MW) exposure guidelines to protect workers and the public: Russia and the West in major conflict." Jan. 18, 2000. EPI1817

163 Democrats in Parliament. Australian Senate Hansard for Feb. 12, 1997. Mobile Phones. EPI1894

164 Wilson, Robert. "What's Cooking?" *The Australian,* March 23, 1999. EPI1883

Europeans have again moved forward in this area ahead of the United States, where the greatest increase in usage is now taking place. "There is now some preliminary scientific evidence that exposures to radiofrequency (RF) radiation may cause subtle effects on biological functions, including those of the brain. This does not necessarily mean that health is affected but it is not possible to say that exposure to RF radiation, even at levels below national guidelines, is totally without potential adverse health effects. The Expert Group has recommended that a precautionary approach to the use of mobile phone technologies be adopted until more detailed and scientifically robust information becomes available.[165]" The standards for exposure are being developed along the lines of the precautionary approach which include the following sections:

> "**Standards.** 1.27 We recommend that, as a precautionary approach, the ICNIRP guidelines for public exposure be adopted for use in the UK rather than the NRPB guidelines.
>
> 1.29 It would be sensible, in line with the precautionary approach, to set in place a long-term follow-up of workers who are occupationally exposed to RF radiation at relatively high levels. We recommend that a register of occupationally exposed workers be established and that cancer risks and mortality be examined to determine whether there are any harmful effects."
>
> "**Advice To Industry.** 1.53 If there are currently unrecognized adverse health effects from the use of mobile phones, children may be more vulnerable because of their developing nervous system, the greater absorption of energy in the tissues of the head, and a longer lifetime of exposure. In line with our precautionary approach, at this time, we believe that the widespread use of mobile phones by children for nonessential calls should be discouraged. We also recommend that the mobile

165 Independent Expert Group on Mobile Phones. "Report on Mobile Phones and Health." May 11, 2000. EPI1892

phone industry should refrain from promoting the use of mobile phones by children."166

The FDA is investigating whether mobile phones can cause cancer, based on two unpublished studies which show a link between cell phone use and cancer. "One study, by the American Health Foundation, in New York, found that mobile phone users had double the risk of developing a certain type of brain tumor than people who did not use them. The second study...found that DNA in human blood cells broke down when exposed to large doses of mobile-phone radiation, possibly laying the genetic groundwork for cancer. 'We are not sure what this means,' said Dr. George Carlo, an epidemiologist who headed the research project from 1993 until last year. 'This could be a colossal coincidence or the tip of the iceberg.'"167

The World Health Organization has identified research needs associated with exposure to RF radiation and makes some interesting observations, again with a great deal of care in implicating risks beyond those already acknowledged by industry:

> "Most studies have examined the results of short-term, whole body exposure to RF fields at levels far higher than those normally associated with wireless communications. With the advent of such devices as walkie-talkies and mobile phones, it has become apparent that few studies address the consequences of localized exposures to RF fields to the head.
>
> **Cancer:** Current scientific evidence indicates that exposure to RF fields, such as those emitted by mobile phones and their base stations, is unlikely to induce or promote cancers.
>
> **Other health risks:** Scientists have reported other effects of using mobile phones including changes in brain activity, reaction times, and sleep patterns.

166 Independent Expert Group on Mobile Phones. "Report on Mobile Phones and Health." May 11, 2000. EPI1892

167 Smith, Karen. "New Evidence Links Mobiles To Cancer." *Wired,* March 30, 2000. EPI1879

Electromagnetic interference: When mobile phones are used close to some medical devices (including pacemakers, implantable defibrillators, and certain hearing aids) there is a possibility of causing interference. There is also the potential of interference between mobile phones and aircraft electronics."168

It is interesting to note that interference with electronic circuits is acknowledged but discussion of the effects on the more sensitive instrument – the human body – is fought vigorously by many.

Reducing the Risk

"'As the EMF/EMR health effects issue becomes more widely known, especially in relation to mobile phone use, there is a corresponding increasing number of so called EMF protective devices being advertised in health and alternative magazines as 'cure-alls' which apparently claim to provide complete protection from exposure to all forms of manmade electromagnetic fields (EMF).' There is a wide range of devices being offered that make all kinds of unsubstantiated claims."169

Earthpulse Press researched the devices being offered and other solutions to the problems related to cell and home portable phone use. We searched for solutions through the Internet and other sources with limited success in finding scientific confirmation of many of the claims of protection. It is not realistic to assume that use can be or should be eliminated as these devices have revolutionized communication and will continue to contribute to change. However, reducing power and radio frequency emissions can also be achieved. Significant work should be put into the effort to determine which emissions are harmful and which can be used to perhaps promote health. There may be carriers and better ways to move the mountains of communications

168 World Health Organization. "Electromagnetic Fields And Public Health." Fact Sheet No. 193, revised June 2000. EPI2090

169 Maisch, Don. Discussion Paper concerning the validity of the science, promotion and sales of EMR Protective Devices. Emfacts Consultancy. Nov. 21, 1999. EPI1802

and information now creating much of our trade and commerce. Some suggestions are as follows:

1. Reduce use is universally regarded as the best step. Use by children should be eliminated. Use in inside spaces like buildings and automobiles increases exposure significantly because of the signal strength required to create a connection from inside a car or building is much greater. Home portable phones should be replaced with the old style hard wired phones and cell phones use significantly reduced.

2. If still using a cell phone or portable home phone keep the phone away from the body when in standby mode. When in use hold the phone as far away from the head as possible. Even one inch can significantly reduce the exposure because the energy density drops very rapidly with distance from the body. Keep the antenna away from the head and pointing away from the body.170 "Radiation from all sources obeys the inverse square law. That is, the further you are from the source the less intense your exposure to the radiation. In fact, it drops off with the square of your distance from the source. If you are twice as far from a fire you feel one quarter of the radiant heat, but if you move four times as far away you only feel one sixteenth of the heat."171

3. Most of the devices being sold to reduce cell phone radiation do not have any science behind them. None of the devices claiming to eliminate **all** emissions had any science behind them and if they truly did eliminate all of the electromagnetic radiation associated with the device the phone would not transmit or receive calls. We were able to find two systems which are supported by science and United States Patents. One of these devices is being marketed under Cell/Wave Guard™. We found that up to 61% of energy emissions could be stopped from entering the body. While this represents a significant reduction it is not known if it is enough to guard against all potential effects.

4. Choose the right phone. When making an initial choice of the phone a person is going to acquire it is important to select a device with the lowest level of emissions. The difference between

170 Helin, Jan. "How Dangerous Is Your Mobile Phone?" *Aftonbladet,* Feb. 8, 1997. EPI1881

171 Wilson, Robert. "What's Cooking?" *The Australian,* March 23, 1999. EPI1883

phone models, even of the same brand name, can be as high as 600%. The best initial selection should be made to minimize exposures. The industry is beginning to pay attention to this issue and many new phones are being designed to reduce radiation exposures. In addition the industry is beginning to label phone packaging in terms of the energy emission considerations.[172, 173]

Solutions to the cell phone and wireless world's side effects must be considered in developing policy on radiation exposures. Significant resources need to be invested in this area in order to create safe exposure levels. Throughout industry significant advances are being made with respect to "connectivity" while risks emerge and are largely ignored or are dealt with as "public relations efforts" rather than public health concerns. It is time for a change.

Is the wireless world creating a public health hazard? We believe precautions are the order of the day.

---

172 CNN, "Cell Phone Industry to Publish Radiation Data", July 17, 2000, http://www.cnn.com/2000/US/07/17/cellphone.01/index.html EPI2207

173 CNN, "Mobile Phones to Feature Radiation Labels Next Year", August 28, 2000, http://www.cnn.com/2000/HEALTH/08/28/health.cellphones.reut/index.html EPI2347

Chapter 4

The Rise of Technology & The Instruments of Control

"Internally, the adversary might be the traitor, the faint of heart, or the fellow traveler – anyone who opposes or is insufficiently cooperative with the leader who controls the means of information warfare."[174]

Information warfare is becoming one of the most intense areas of military research – it is the "technology of political control" often referenced by European researchers, politicians and others. In this war, the United States attacks the heart of an adversary's command and control systems by manipulating information flows. These systems are highly vulnerable to attack. The war on information can be waged against domestic and international threats and is undetectable in most cases. "The technology of political control is a new type of weaponry. It is the product of the application of science and technology to the problem of neutralizing the state's internal enemies. It is mainly directed at civilian populations, and it is not intended to kill (and only rarely does). It is aimed as much at hearts and minds as at bodies."[175] This subject area overlaps several others and should be contemplated in conjunction with other technologies when visualizing the effects of these new weapons. From civil protest to Internet surfing, government control of information is the objective.

---

174. Szafranski, Col. Richard (USAF). "A Theory of Information Warfare: Preparing For 2020." *Air Chronicles* EPI232

175. Ackroyd, Carol et al. *The Technology of Political Control.* Penguin Books, New York, 1997. ISBN 0 14 02.1943 9. EPI842

The European Position

This issue has become a significant topic for debate in the European community and has drawn the attention and alarm of elected officials around the world. The issues surrounding this technology include privacy questions, economic power and ethical issues. The European concerns are summarized below:

Executive Summary

> "**Innovations in Crowd Control Weapons:** This section briefly analyses recent innovations in crowd control weapons (including the evolution of a 2nd generation of so called 'less-lethal weapons' from nuclear labs in the USA) and concludes that they are dubious weapons based on dubious and secret research. The Commission should be requested to report to Parliament on the existence of formal liaison arrangements between the EU and the USA to introduce such weapons for use in streets and prisons here. The EU has also recommended to (i) establish objective common criteria for assessing the biomedical effects of all so called less lethal weapons and ensure any future authorization is based on independent research; (ii) ensure that all research used to justify the deployment on any new crowd control weapon in the EU is published in the open scientific press and subject to independent scientific scrutiny, before any authorization is given to deploy. In the meantime the Parliament is asked to reaffirm its current ban on plastic bullets and that all deployment of devices using pepper gas (OC) be halted until such a time as independent European research on its risks has been undertaken and published.
>
> **The Role & Function of Political Control Technologies:** New police technologies are perceived to be one of the most important factors in attempting substrate conflict control. Such 'control' is viewed as more apparent than real, but serves the purpose of disguising the level of coercive repression being applied. This school of thought argues that once operationally deployed, these technologies exert a profound effect on the character of policing. Whether these changes are symptom or cause of the ensuing change in policing organizations, a major premise of this school of thought is

that a range of unforeseen impacts are associated with the process of integrating these technologies into a society's social, political and cultural control systems.

The full implications of such developments may take time to assess but they are often more important and far reaching than the first order intended effects. It is argued that one impact of this process is the militarization of the police and the para-militarization of the military as their roles, equipment and procedures begin to overlap. This phenomena is seen as having far reaching consequences on the way that future episodes of substrate violence is handled, and influencing whether those involved are reconciled, managed, repressed, 'lost' or efficiently destroyed. Police telematics and their use of databanks (the subject of an earlier STOA report in this area) for example, facilitate prophylactic or preemptive policing as 'dataveillance' is harnessed to target certain strata or classes of people rather than resolve individual crimes. (E.g. the proposed introduction of the Eurodac system which will utilize biometric identification to control and restrict the entry of all Asylum seekers into Europe, building in the process a new technopolitics of exclusion). New surveillance technology can exert a powerful 'chill effect' on those who might wish to take a dissenting view and few will risk exercising their right to democratic protest if the cost is punitive riot policing with equipment which may lead to permanent injury or loss of life.

Recent Trends & Innovations: Automatic fingerprint readers are now common place, and many European companies make them. But any unique attribute of anatomy or personal style can be used to create a human identity recognition system. For example Cellmark Diagnostics (UK) can recognize genes; Mastiff Security Systems (UK) can recognize odor; Hagen Cy-Com (UK) and Eyedentify Inc. (USA) can recognize the pattern of capillaries at the back of the retina; whilst AEA Technology (UK) are capable of signature verification. Over 109 companies in Europe are known to be supplying such biometric systems. DNA fingerprinting is now a reality and Britain has set up the first DNA databank, and has already carried out mass dawn raids of over 1000 people as targeted suspects. Plans are being drawn up by at least one political party to DNA profile the nation from birth. The leading edge companies are racing towards developing face recognition systems which they see as being able to revolutionize crime, customs and intruder detection as well as service access control. Whilst fully reliable systems are perhaps five years off, prototype systems have been developed in France, Germany, the UK and the USA.

Night vision technology developed as a result of the Vietnam war has now been adapted for police usage. Particularly successful are the heli-tele surveillance versions which allow cameras to track human heat signatures in total darkness. The art of bugging has been made significantly easier by a rapidly advancing technology and there is a burgeoning European market. Many systems, do not even require physical entry into the home or office. For those who can secure access to their target room, there is a plethora of devices, many prepackaged to fit into phones, look like cigarette packets or light fittings and some, like the ever popular PK 805 and PK 250, that can be tuned into from a suitable radio. However, the next generation of covert audio bugs are remotely operated, for example the multi-room monitoring system of Lorraine Electronics called DIAL (Direct Intelligent Access Listening) allows an operator to monitor several rooms from anywhere in the world without effecting an illegal entry. Up to four concealed microphones are connected to the subscribers line and these can be remotely activated by simply making a coded telephone call to the target building. Neural Network Bugs go one step further. Built like a small cockroach, as soon as the lights go out they can crawl to the best location for surveillance. In fact Japanese researchers have taken this idea one step further, controlling and manipulating real cockroaches by implanting microprocessors and electrodes in their bodies. The insects can be fitted with micro cameras and sensors to reach the places other bugs can't reach. Passive Millimeter Wave Imaging developed by the US Millitech corporation can scan people from up to 12 feet away and see through clothing to detect concealed items such as weapons, packages and other contraband. Variations of this through-clothing human screening under development (by such companies as the US Raytheon Co.), include systems which illuminate an individual with a low-intensity electromagnetic pulse. A three side very-low X-ray system for human usage, in fixed sites such as prisons, is being developed by Nicolet Imaging Systems of San Diego. Electronic monitoring of offenders or 'tagging', where the subject wears an electronic bracelet which can detect if they have relocated from their home after certain hours etc. has entered into use in the 1990's after being developed to regulate prison populations in the USA. Satellite tracking of VIP's, vehicles etc. is now facilitated by the once military Global-Positioning System (GPS) which is now available for commercial uses.

Dataveillance: The use of telematics by the police has revolutionized policing in the last decade and created the shift towards preemptive policing.

Using data profilers, torturing states have used these systems to compile death lists. For example, the Tadiran computer supplied to Guatemala and installed in the control center of the national palace. According to a senior Guatemala military official, 'the complex contains an archive and a computer file on journalists, students, leaders, people on the left, politicians and so on. Meetings were held in the annex to select assassination victims.' A US priest who fled the country after appearing on such a death list said, 'They had printout lists at the border crossings and at the airport. Once you got on that – then its like bounty hunters.' Within Europe, systems, such as that produced by Harlequin, allow the automatic production of maps of who phoned whom to show friendship networks. Other companies such as Memex described above, allow entire life profiles of virtually anyone in a state having an official existence. Photographs and video material can be included in the record and typically up to 700 other databases can be covered at any one time, to extend the data profile in real time. Significant changes in the capacity of new surveillance systems can be anticipated with the advent of new materials such as Buckminster

Fullerene, which will lead to miniaturization of systems by several orders of magnitude.

Discreet Order Vehicles: Hundreds of companies are now manufacturing police and internal security vehicles in Europe. The newer companies entering the market for law enforcement vehicles tend to manufacture for both military and police purposes (eg armored personnel carriers, patrol, riot control, mobile prison, perimeter patrol, etc.) and configured to have a 'non-aggressive design'. In real terms this means that their external appearance rather than their operational characteristics are modified to give a non-threatening appearance. Such 'discreet order vehicles' look benign – like ambulances, whilst retaining a retaliatory capacity, capable of dispersing or capturing dissident groups or individuals. Some models like the Talon incorporate repellent electrified panels as well as a weapons capacity such as water cannon. Such vehicles are frequently used to seal people into a dispersal zone where the riot squads are at work, rather than chase them out.

Less Lethal Weapons: ....the essential role of new crowd control weapons and tactics is to amplify the level of aggression that can be unleashed by an individual officer. Thus the same rationale lies behind the use of the new US side handle batons, the use of horse, riot shield charges using riot wedges and snatch squads and the new martial arts style arrest techniques which, entered European policing training in the mid 1980s. The biggest growth area has been in what used to be called 'non-lethal weapons.' The fact that some of these weapons kill, blind, scalp and permanently maim led the authorities and manufacturers to act – they came up with a new name – 'less-lethal weapons' – i.e. they only sometimes kill. Again a PR objective is catered for in the names which sound as if the security forces are using relative restraint. Whether it be Belfast or Beijing, these technologies are converging around the same design types...this area has seen prodigious innovation including a second generation of new weapon types being produced in the former nuclear weapon laboratories of the US in conjunction with big business.

Individually these weapons are becoming more powerful. For example, each new riot agent is more powerful than the one it replaces. Thus CS is nearly 20 times more powerful than the CN it replaced; CR is more than 30 times more powerful than CN and the newest and most aggressively marketed agent, OC, the most powerful of them all. Little notice has been taken of the professional hazard assessments of the most commonly used kinetic impact weapons deployed in Europe and the USA which have consequences in the 'dangerous or severe damage region'.

Lethal Weapons: In theory, police weapons should have a different level of lethality and penetration compared with those used by the military. In urban settings there is always the risk of hitting passers-by and if a round has high velocity and penetration, it will easily pass through an intended target and continue penetrating walls and go on and perhaps kill innocents beyond the observed fire zone. To obviate this problem, manufacturers are increasingly producing hollow point, expanding, or 'dum-dum' ammunition for police and special forces use. Paradoxically, the Hague Declaration of 1989, which prohibited the use of hollow point or dum-dum ammunition, does not apply to the policing of civil conflicts. Soft nosed ammunition which mushrooms in the body, causes far more serious damage than ordinary ammunition. Dum-dums would take an arm or a leg off, whereas ordinary ammunition would sail through leaving a relatively clean hole. Some [of] these weapons like Winchester's Black Talon or the high explosive filled pre-fragmented Frag 12 cause horrific injuries and raise serious questions about due process and the right to a fair trial since without immediate medical attention, a target would be effectively an extra-judicial execution. Many companies are now producing these bullets in Europe.

Developments In Surveillance Technology: 'Subtler and more far reaching means of invading privacy have become available to the government. Discovery and invention have made it possible for the government, by means far more effective than stretching upon the rack, to obtain disclosure in court of what is whispered in the closet.'

Second Generation Incapacitation Weapons: Thus a second generation of kinetic, chemical, optico-acoustic, microwave, disabling and paralyzing technologies is on the horizon, to join the existing arsenal of weapons designed for public order control. Much of the initial new work has been undertaken in US nuclear laboratories such as Oak Ridge, Lawrence Livermore and Los Alamos. Many cynics see the work as a rice bowl initiative with scientists looking for new weapons projects to justify their future careers as the cold war made their old skill redundant. Already they have come up with a Pandora's box of new technologies. These include:

* Ultra-sound generators, which cause disorientation, vomiting and involuntary defecation, disturbing the ear system which controls balance and inducing nausea. The system which uses two speakers can target individuals in a crowd.

* Visual stimulus and illusion techniques such as high intensity strobes which pulse in the critical epileptic fit-inducing flashing frequency and holograms used to project active camouflage.

* Reduced energy kinetic weapons. Variants on the bean bag philosophy which ostensibly will result in no damage (similar claims were once made about plastic bullets).

* New disabling, calmative, sleep inducing agents mixed with DMSO which enables the agent to quickly cross the skin barrier and an extensive range of pain causing, paralyzing and foul-smelling area denial chemicals. Some of these are chemically engineered variants of the heroin molecule. They work extremely rapidly, one touch and disablement follows. Yet one person's tranquilization may be another's lethal dose.

* Microwave and acoustic disabling systems.

* Human capture nets which can be laced with chemical irritant or electrified to pack an extra punch.

* Lick 'em and stick 'em technology such as the Sandia National Laboratory's foam gun which expands to between 35-50 times its original volume. It's extremely sticky, gluing together the target's feet and hands to the pavement.

* Aqueous barrier foam which can be laced with pepper spray.

* Blinding laser weapons and Isotrophic radiator shells which use superheated gaseous plasma to produce a dazzling burst of laser like light.

* Thermal guns which incapacitate through a wall by raising body temperature to 107 degrees.

* Magnetosphere gun which delivers what feels like a blow to the head.

We are no longer at a theoretical stage with these weapons. US companies are already piloting new systems, lobbying hard and where possible, laying down potentially lucrative patents. For example, last year *New Scientist* reported that the American Technology Corporation (ATC) of Poway, California has used what it calls acoustic heterodyning technology to target individuals in a crowd with infra-sound to pinpoint an individual 200-300 metres away. The system can also project sonic holograms which can conjure audio messages out of thin air so just one person hears.

Critics of such projects suggest that non-lethal war is a contradiction in terms. Many of the so called non-lethal weapons are in reality far from non-lethal. They can and have killed, maimed, blinded and scalped innocent bystanders. There is a real danger that they will make conflicts more lethal by enraging crowds and by paralyzing people making them more vulnerable to other operations by the military and security forces. In that sense these weapons could be considered pre-lethal and actually lead to higher casualty rates. In fact the US proponents of these weapons are under no illusions. Their focus is not to replace lethal munitions but to augment existing and future capabilities which will provide a spectrum of force response options. The area most commentators have not addressed is the extent that such weapons will help the military create new roles for themselves as part of internal policing operations.

Recommendations: ...The commission should be requested to report on the existing liaison arrangements for the second generation of non-lethal weapons to enter European Union from the USA and call for an independent report on their alleged safety as well as their intended and unforeseen social and political effects. During the interim period, deployment by the police, the military or paramilitary special forces, of US made or licensed chemical irritant, kinetic, acoustic, laser, electro-magnetic frequency, capture, entanglement, injector or electrical disabling and paralyzing weapons, should be prohibited within Europe.

The European Parliament should (a) Note the biased research on Peppergas (OC) undertaken by corrupt FBI officials and the continuing use of FBI safety assurances in other countries on the basis of this flawed research: (b) Call for a ban on Peppergas (OC) deployment or usage within EU member states, until new independent research on OC is undertaken.

New Prison Control Systems: Critics such as Lilly & Knepper argue that in examining the international aspects of crime control as industry, more attention is needed to the changing activities of the companies which used to provide supplies to the military. At the end of the cold war, 'with defense contractors reporting declines in sales, the search for new markets is pushing corporate decision making, it should be no surprise to see increased corporate activity in criminal justice.' Where such companies previously profited from wars with foreign enemies, they are increasingly turning their energy to the

> new opportunities afforded by crime control as industry. Increasingly in the US, we witness the trend toward private prisons and the critical issue here is can the privatization of prison control create a rehabilitation process if its dominant raison d'etre is profit from control systems and hence cost cutting."[176]

Our own experience with the European Parliament suggests that in order to compile such a report significant evidence had to be presented to prove the actual state of development of these technologies. Moreover, their concerns are the same concerns which are voiced whenever these technologies are scrutinized by anyone concerned about human rights issues and the migration of power from military to law enforcement organizations. In February 1997, I presented testimony and a demonstration of an infra-sound device in an open hearing of a subcommittee of the Foreign Affairs Committee of the European Parliament in Brussels. During the hearing we were able to bring Members of Parliament (MPs) significant data on the development of these technologies.

Since the publication of the above Executive Summary a great deal has happened. September 11, 2001 changed the face of the world by injecting a sufficient level of fear to bring about the introduction of these technologies. In the case of gas over 100 people died in the 2002 winter hostage crisis in Moscow where not only gas was used but its counter neutralizing compounds were not available to treat the many civilians who died.

The Technology Revolution

New computing power which will dwarf the existing technology is only a few years away. These new abilities in compiling and sorting information will lead to ever increasing control of populations through political, military or commercial purposes. "A team of UCLA chemists and researchers at Hewlett-Packard Laboratories recently reported taking a significant step toward producing computers that will be molecular rather than silicon based...'We can potentially get the computational power of 100 workstations on the size of a grain of

176. European Parliament. "An Appraisal of Technologies of Political Control, Interim Study." STOA, Jan. 19, 1998. EPI1157

sand,' Heath said..."[177] These advances will magnify the efforts of the military and policing organizations many times beyond what is presented in these pages. At the same time if properly used it will lead to incredible scientific, educational and humanitarian uses. Full and open disclosure and discussion will be critical if shared human values are to be a part of the platform on which our science and society rests.

The advent of modern weapons, including Information Warfare (IW) systems, will change the way wars will be fought in the future. "As a nation that holds the value of human life and freedoms high, the US must prepare to deal with 'nonlethal' attacks, which have the capability to not only cause economic chaos and loss of life, but impinge on freedoms we take for granted, yet hold so dear. As a result, when confronted with an IW scenario, whether in peacetime or conflict, we must be prepared to respond appropriately. However, our responses must comply with various factors, including international laws, treaties and neutrality considerations. Whether in peacetime or a hostile environment, our responses should be no less decisive if an adversary threatens our national security interests. Should an adversary caught waging IW, in 'peacetime,' to influence policy and affect our national security, be held any less accountable than an adversary who, in 'peacetime,' explodes a bomb in a German nightclub, an aircraft in midair, or a building killing 240 marines, with the same objectives?"[178] These are interesting questions raised by military planners – questions which should be answered by public debate in forums where accountability can be assured.

Information Technology – The Ease of War

Several emerging technologies will have profound impacts on society. There are three that stand out as the most important – infotechnology, biotechnology, and nanotechnology. These technologies will have incredible positive impacts on people as well as the potential of misuse as is the case with many innovations. As

177. Wolpert, Stuart. *UCLA Today*. "Dawn of Molecular Computer." http://www.today.ucla.edu/html/990727dawn.html EPI140
178. Miller, Maj. Robert. *International Law: How It Affects Rules Of Engagement And Responses In Information Warfare*. March 1997. The Research Department, Air Command and Staff College. AU/ACSC/0217/97-03. EPI784

these three areas merge into a new super-technology the division between living creatures and machines will become increasingly less clear.

Information systems when coupled with the advent of nanotechnology (scaled down to a factor of a billion) will allow for super small devices. These devices when added to living creatures, people or human created life will increase the complexity of machines and their uses. Biotechnology when merged in this way, which is already occurring, will again place new issues of fair use, medical ethics and questions of life itself in front of those making the decisions. Who should make these decisions – citizens, corporations, politicians, scientists, military planners or others?

Information technology has been the subject of much consideration. Military vision statements attempt to predict how new breakthroughs in information technologies will affect warfighting. Some of the immediate effects are already evident in military operations in shaping the way wars are fought. The changes in levels of technology from the Gulf War, to Kosovo, and more recently, Afghanistan where the most incredible use of new information technologies were deployed is now evident to all.

The changes in warfare have created a situation where combatants, from the countries possessing high levels of technology, are increasingly removed from the battlefield. These technologies save American lives but change the way veterans experience war. In the past the smell of death, the visual images and experience caused veterans to work hard to assure that future wars were only engaged as a true last resort. Returning vets understood the results of war from their firsthand experience. Today's wars keep superpower combatants out of harms way while inflicting total destruction on adversaries. While wars will continue to occur in the future our willingness to use military might in warfare increases as the ease of inflicting destruction improves with innovation. War is no longer a last resort but is being used more often with greater ferocity. The concept of "preemptive strikes" is now being pressed by the second Bush administration. The point I am attempting to make here is that the superpowers and their citizens need to clearly contemplate the need for war rather than diplomacy, and exercise appropriate restraint. This does not mean that war will be avoided but increases the probability that it will truly be engaged only when really a last remaining option.

The other side of information advances is that it shifts power with greater ease. Innovation potential is universal with human beings, as part of our creative capacity. The ease of information flow has increased the likelihood of wider distribution of technology and consequently both beneficial as well as more sinister uses become possible. We are at a point in human development where these mutually reinforcing advances will combine to produce a result so very different from what we now know that it is impossible to predict the actual outcomes. However, some near term consequences can be predicted. The foremost consequence will be a diffusion of power. This diffusion of power will make the world a more dangerous place. "There is a wide variety of violence-prone groups that could take advantage of power diffusion and, in so doing, disrupt nations at all levels of development. A list suggested by Steven Metz includes organized crime, private armies, urban gangs, insurgents, regional separatists, conspiracy theory terrorists, radical cults, neo-Luddites, and violent environmentalists. To this list one might add antigovernment militias and the 'hobbyists' who disrupt information systems as a form of recreation."[179]

The above quoted article predicts the continual breakup of nation states into smaller and smaller regionally independent countries such as what we have witnessed in the former Soviet Union and Yugoslavia, partly as a result of increases in technology making it possible for these groups to break away. As a result, the possibility of intervention by others in order to stabilize an area is becoming increasingly likely. It is expected that the next 20 years will see an increase in these kinds of conflicts and interventions. The expected diffusion of power will make these military missions much more dangerous.

Given the current state of information technology it is now possible to monitor virtually all electronic transmissions from radio to e-mail. The same progress will soon make it possible to conduct full-time remote surveillance of any geographic area.

179. Adams, Thomas K. "Radical Destabilizing Effects of New Technologies." *Parameters*, Autumn 1998. EPI768

Sub-miniature video 'cameras on a chip' for such systems are cheap and available now and are shrinking in size every few months. Soon the use of these types of cameras manned by automated systems will make it possible to monitor an entire city or, given the motivation and the money, an entire country. These systems are being installed as crime prevention measures but will have the effect of stripping the anonymity of private citizens. It was shown in our earlier book *Earth Rising – The Revolution* that these technologies are being used with increasing frequency and, since September 11, 2001, the pace has accelerated. The cost of these technologies is also dropping as raw materials and new manufacturing systems are discovered and brought on-line. Just like data storage for computers increased exponentially in the last five decades we will see the same in all areas including this one only now it requires only months rather than decades to realize these kinds of changes.

The combinations of these new technological areas are blurred in the sense that they merge into one technological event. The miniaturization of information systems and combining them with living matter is already underway. Today it is possible to actually grow brain cells on a computer chip for possible use in information processing. The opportunities present in innovation are only well served when positive human values drive innovations. Our technology can either serve humankind like a delivery truck bringing our daily mail or can be used to destroy us like a suicide bomber driving that same truck.

Infowar

"Information warfare is believed by many to be the means by which the next 'big' war will be fought and, more importantly, the means by which future wars will be won."180 "Although the technology is cloaked in secrecy, a wide range of US weapons designed to conduct offensive computer warfare is under development, a handful have been tested and at least one has been used in combat."181 Maintaining the "order of battle requires a system for managing and communicating information. Today, the system is

180. Aldrich, Maj. Richard W. "The International Legal Implications of Information Warfare." *Airpower Journal*, Fall 1996, pp. 99-110. EPI349
181. Fulghum, David. "New Weapons Slowed By Secrecy Clampdown." *Aviation Week & Space Technology*, Jan. 19, 1998. EPI197

called command, control, communications, computers, and intelligence (C4I)..."[182] In the aftermath of the attack on the World Trade Centers in New York some of the vulnerabilities of the electronic revolution began to be considered. From data exchanges to financial transfers these systems were used by terrorists as a means for conducting their business. These systems were also the most vulnerable for them as assets began to be seized and communications intercepted. Quickly these adversaries stopped the use of these technologies in exchange for older less accessible systems like couriers, mail and direct contact on a person-to-person basis.

As the United States and others build modern defense systems based on technology, dependence on these systems creates new risks. The very technology that we are developing are the most vulnerable to tampering and interference at a distance, using modern technology against modern technology.

The conventional wars of the past required massive power to inflict the kind of destruction which can now be done with a few key strokes of a computer. A strike against information systems could destroy economies, cripple modern armies and shut down communication systems among other things.

The military has established their own center for the development of information warfare for both defensive and offensive purposes: "The 609th's primary role may be defensive at this stage, but information can clearly be an offensive weapon too – though the military is generally far less eager to discuss that side of the cybercoin. Much of that research is occurring further up the military ladder, in this case at the Air Force's Air Intelligence Agency (AIA) and its Information Warfare Center at Kelly AFB in San Antonio, Texas."[183] The use of this technology implies the direct interference with private communications even outside of declared open conflict. "Quiet wars" like those waged in Guatemala, Cambodia, Cuba, during the Soviet war in Afghanistan or perhaps even some uncooperative western state all represent targets of undeclared Infowars.

---

182. Maethner et al. *Worldwide information control system.* Air Force 2025. April 1996. EPI781

183. O'Malley, Chris. "Information Warriors of the 609th." *Popular Science,* July 1997. EPI666

Infowar is already here in the sense that computer hacking has become commonplace, with government resources often the target. Even our former foes may have freelance hackers slicing into our systems according to the following report. "The FBI is trying to determine whether cyberspies at Moscow's prestigious Russian Academy of Sciences are responsible for Moonlight Maze, the most pervasive assault yet on sensitive US Defense Department and other computer networks."184 Meanwhile, "The Pentagon has stepped up cyberdefense and is planning cybercombat. The FBI is still struggling to unravel Moonlight Maze, a massive assault on US government computers that has been traced to Russia. Prodded by the White House, other agencies are also scrambling to protect America's electronic infrastructure from a daily digital barrage from around the world."185

The United States is advancing its plans for Information Warfare (IO) in terms of its own offensive capabilities. "Offensive IO involve the integrated use of assigned and supporting capabilities and activities, mutually supported by intelligence, to affect adversary decision makers and achieve or promote specific objectives. These assigned and supporting capabilities and activities include, but are not limited to, operations security (OPSEC), military deception, psychological operations, electronic warfare (EW), physical attack/destruction, and special information operations (SIO), and may include computer network attack. Offensive IO may be conducted in a variety of situations and circumstances across the range of military operations and may have their greatest impact in peace and the initial stages of a crisis. Beyond the threshold of crisis, Offensive IO can be a critical force enabler..."186 What this says is that these systems are part of the modern war making machine as well as an area in which our own systems remain exposed. Increased methods of protecting these systems is an area of intense research.

---

184. Drogin, Bob. "FBI traces '98 siege to Russia sites." *Anchorage Daily News*, Nov. 14, 1999. EPI1230

185. Drogin, Bob. "Cyberspace emerges as new battleground." *Anchorage Daily News*, Nov. 14, 1999. EPI1231

186. Joint Chiefs of Staff. Joint Doctrine for Information Operations. Joint Pub 3-13. Oct. 9, 1998. EPI174

One branch of the military is engaged in significant increases in their use of the Internet that not only will improve their efficiency but also increase their exposure to interference through adversarial Information Operations (IO). "The navy plans to use a radical strategy to build its much-anticipated mega-intranet, which will provide 450,000 users worldwide with items ranging from PCs to communication pipes and cost as much as $2.2 billion. In an industry briefing set for July 7, the Navy plans to back what it described as a 'sweeping shift' in its information technology infrastructure and management."187 "The computerization of the battlefield is one of two technology trends that military experts expect will revolutionize warfare in the decades ahead. As the US National Research Council puts it: 'A whole new form of warfare will evolve, based on the use of [computers] and on methods to attack, deceive, and neutralize them.'"188 This type of engagement works both ways – as we increase our capacity we also increase our vulnerability to attack in information warfare (IW). "Will IW be a new but subordinate facet of warfare in which the United States and its allies readily overcome their own potential cyberspace weaknesses and gain and sustain whatever tactical and strategic military advantages that might be available in this arena? Or will the changes in conflict wrought by the ongoing information revolution be so rapid and profound that the net result is a new and grave threat to traditional military operations and US society that fundamentally changes the future character of warfare?"189 "The latest information warfare discussion has seen the emergence of a new framework for understanding emerging weaknesses. In keeping with the new focus on homeland infrastructure (and military system support infrastructure) protection, the actors of primary importance as potential adversaries in information conflict have also shifted."190 "Protecting our critical infrastructures in the Information Age raises new challenges for all of us. Above all, it requires a partnership between the government and private industry to

187. Brewin, Bob and Verton, Daniel. "Navy kicks off radical intranet buy." *Federal Computer Week*, June 28, 1999. EPI1115

188. Gunther, Judith et al. "The Digital Warrior." *Popular Science*, Sept. 1994, pp. 60-64, 89. EPI38

189. Molander, Roger C. et al. "Strategic Information Warfare: A New Face of War." Rand, 1996. EPI280

190. Mussington, David. "Information Warfare: a maturing issue area." *Defence & Security Review*, 1999. EPI501

reduce our vulnerability to attack and increase our capabilities to respond to new threats."[191]

The Information Police

The need for some regulation of the Internet may be appropriate but the idea of comprehensive and full surveillance goes too far. The NSA currently monitors the activity of all Internet users through their networks with other countries. This effort is cloaked in the theme of "its for your own protection" but offers great opportunities for undetected abuse by government agencies. Already, "Congress has attempted to regulate the Web with legislation designed to protect organizations involved in interstate commerce. Under current guidelines, state and local officers are obliged to apply their penal codes to prosecute Internet criminals."[192]

As the problems are identified the shut down of hackers is increasing and welcomed by many who have been victimized by these lone rangers. This also points out the problems which are posed by individuals with access to very sophisticated technology which even the very young can manipulate with ease. "Raids by a new FBI cybercrime unit against those individuals suspected of meddling with computer networks and Web sites has prompted a counteroffensive of sorts by various groups of hackers who have vandalized several corporate and government Web sites, including an agency site. Paul Maidmen, 18, a New Jersey hacking suspect who was raided and had his computer and related components seized, said, 'I have never defaced any Web pages or taken out any major sites.' The unit also has requested documents from two Internet service providers. John Vranesevich, operator of a Web site that chronicles hacker activity, said the information requested involved software tools, computer files, and aliases, and that overall, 'it's an uninformed investigation.'"[193]

---

191. Vatis, Michael. A Message from Michael Vatis, Director of the National Infrastructure Protection Center. http://www.fbi.gov/nipc/nipc.com EPI552
192. Sullivan, Scott. "Policing the Internet." *FBI Law Enforcement Bulletin,* June, 1999. Vol. 68, No. 6. Source: NLECTC *Law Enforcement & Technology News Summary,* July 8, 1999. EPI931
193. Richtel, Matt. "Federal Cybercrime Unit." *New York Times,* May 19, 1999. Source: NLECTC *Law Enforcement & Technology News Summary,* June 3, 1999. EPI957

Once again it is a two-way street where both villain and police can equally access the systems. "If criminals are going to use the Internet to commit crime, then law enforcement officials are going to use it to catch them, according to Ron Horack, an investigator in the Loundoun County, Va. sheriffs office. Police are tracking the online activities of suspects, sometimes even victims, seizing evidence from Internet Service Providers (ISPs) or other Internet services and turning public what some criminals hiding behind screen names thought was a secret. Marc Rotenberg, executive director of the Electronic Privacy Information Center, says the intrusion into communications is a threat to privacy, and thinks law enforcement should use traditional tools for conducting investigations, such as stings, informants, and forensic evidence."194 While some argue against use of electronically collected evidence there is a need to be able to access data when proper warrants have been issued. The increase in the ability of criminals to otherwise have a huge advantage in their illegal activity is obvious. In the environment of fear created in the aftermath of the terrorists attacks on New York the Patriot Bill was passed which has led to a number of initiatives to intercept communications for collecting "soft intelligence". This is casting an ever widening net in the hope of catching the bad guys while trampling over the very rights we are theoretically trying to protect. Striking a balance in an environment where fear is removed as the driving force will be the challenge in coming days for democracies around the world who are trading freedom for the illusion of security.

Very complex software systems are being developed to allow greater visibility of those engaged in suspicious activity. While the systems are far from perfect, they will allow the most obvious hackers to be apprehended. "The Tiresias system – software originally developed by IBM to search DNA strands for recurring patterns – can be used to monitor networks for hacker activity. The software uses a pattern-matching algorithm that can sift through data and identify strings of data such as a hacker trying scores of passwords to break into a system. The system first monitors a system before it is hooked up to a network, identifies a pattern of 'good' activity, and later can identify

194. Woodward, Calvin. "In Investigations, Online Activities Can Become an Open Book." *Detroit Free Press Online,* May 31, 1999. Source: NLECTC *Law Enforcement & Technology News Summary,* June 3, 1999. EPI959

abnormal patterns, such as would be created by a hacker."[195] Europeans are also setting up their own systems for catching cyber-criminals. "Germany has unveiled a dedicated Internet search engine with the aim of boosting law enforcement officials' ability to monitor online crime. The engine helps crack down on the transmission of illegal online material by enabling police to find evidence of such doings, as well as the names and addresses of the responsible lawbreakers."[196] These systems are now receiving massive funding as one of the key modern infrastructures in need of protection.

The big problem with government monitoring is that it is being abused. The concern deals with the balance of safety and security -vs- privacy and individual freedom. The debate must be engaged and the limits of government strictly defined in the law, something yet to be done on several levels.

I was victimized by the misuse of information systems when someone took my identity and set up a website to attempt to destroy my reputation. When local police were called in there was no law on the books in Alaska which could be used to bring law enforcement into the picture. When the FBI was called they passed me to the Federal Trade Commission who was only collecting data but not pursuing prosecution of the criminals even though we had the villains internet address. We were told that if more primitive methods had been used, like the mail or telephone, then local law enforcement could have gotten involved as a harassment case but the Internet was not covered by local law. The rush to break down privacy in support of government surveillance capabilities has not been in balance with the need for protection of individual citizens. This must change. As technology evolves protection from abuse, misuse and direct assaults needs to be also created.

Propaganda Wars

Propaganda has been used throughout history in waging war. It reached a new level during World War II when both allies

---

195. *London Sunday Times Online.* "All Seeing Software Keeps Eye on Hackers." Sept. 8, 1998. Source: NLECTC *Law Enforcement & Technology News Summary,* Nov. 11, 1998. EPI1075

196. Wadsworth, Stafford. "Crime Busting Search Engine for Germany's Internet Cops." *InternetNews.com,* May 19, 1999. Source: NLECTC *Law Enforcement & Technology News Summary,* June 3, 1999. EPI961

and axis powers exploited the prejudices and biases of their respective populations in order to gain support for the war. Carefully controlled media and press reports were the working tools of all governments at the time. The use of propaganda has become standard fare for politicians, corporations and individuals in the 21st century often going unchallenged by the real facts. Even more sophisticated psychological manipulation now takes place. America's $100 million studio in the sky is now "capable of overriding radio and television transmissions in another nation and substituting taped US – produced programs. Such psychological warfare operations were used during Operation Desert Storm to persuade Iraqi soldiers to surrender. Other 'psyops': Operation Urgent Fury in Grenada and Operation Uphold Democracy in Haiti."[197] In another report "Air Force Mission: Commando Solo conducts psychological operations and civil affairs broadcast missions in the standard AM, FM, HF, TV and military communications bands. Missions are flown at maximum altitudes possible to ensure optimum propagation patterns. The targets may be either military or civilian personnel."[198] It is a great deal more effective than "Radio Free Europe" ever was. In wartime it may be fair but could it be used in other "national emergencies" or internal conflicts?

This book is in part the outgrowth of the Internet in that the Web has provided a means for collecting and organizing information which was not possible even ten years ago. The idea of bringing together diverse people around common issues is the most valuable aspect of the Internet. This tool provides people an unprecedented opportunity to influence and impact the evolution of international dialogue. The power of the Net is such that it is giving people a new forum for democratic dialogue and perhaps an increase in cooperation between average people rather than politicians. The military is also looking at ways to use and interfere with this dialogue. It is critical to keep in mind that the interference with information through disinformation is already part of the military program. The idea that some unknown person may be deciding who is a threat and interfering with their information flow should be alarming because the military's view

197 Weeks, George. "Sen. Levin wants 'Commando Solo' in skies over Bosnia to counter Karadzic." Detroit News, Aug. 12, 1997. EPI793

198. EC-130 Commando Solo. http://hqafsoc.hurlburt.af.mil/ec-130.html EPI792

of who is a threat and the Constitution's ideas of freedom may come in direct conflict. A revealing summary of these ideas follows:

> "The political process is moving onto the Internet. Both within the United States and internationally, individuals, interest groups, and even nations are using the Internet to find each other, discuss the issues, and further their political goals. The Internet has also played an important role in recent conflicts. As a result, overseas segments of the Internet can be a useful tool for DoD (Department of Defense), both for gathering and disseminating information. By monitoring public message traffic and alternative news sources from around the world, early warning of impending significant developments can be developed, in advance of more traditional means of indications and warning. Commentary placed on the Internet by observers on the scene of low-intensity conflicts overseas could be useful to US policy making. During larger scale conflicts, when other conventional channels are disrupted, the Internet can be the only available means of communication into and out of affected areas. Internet messages originating within regions under authoritarian control could provide other useful intelligence. Public messages conveying information about the intent of overseas groups prone to disrupting US military operations can provide important counterintelligence. The Internet could also be used to help achieve unconventional warfare objectives. Used creatively as an integral asset, the Internet can facilitate many DoD operations and activities."199

"Equally unsettling is the internal aspect of this redefining of the relationship between politics and war. The danger of reversing Clasuswitz's ideas on civil–military relationships clearly emerges in the writing of another 'information war' advocate, who argues that one of the promises of information war is that 'at last, our military planners can be freed of political constraints.' This concept of information warfare is very dangerous from a civil liberties point of view.

---

199. Swett, Charles. *Strategic Assessment: The Internet.* Office of the Assistant Secretary of Defense for Special Operations and Low-Intensity Conflict. July 17, 1995. EPI782

Unfortunately, information war has become so expansive a term that it now threatens to become a tautology by encompassing nearly everything beyond the most primitive forms of combat. Some include traditional intelligence as information warfare, while others include the capabilities inherent in certain weapons systems. Others see the decision to interfere in Somalia as an example of successful information war, presumably by the administration's internal foes who preferred that we intervene there rather than in Sudan, the site of much worse disasters. This logic could be extended to acts of politics, advances in weaponry, and uses of propaganda. Indeed, the use of high-tech propaganda, some quite fanciful, is a major theme of some information war advocates.

This reliance upon new and old forms of propaganda, while attractive for those who wish to substitute a new form of mind control for violence, is yet another weakness of information war."200

"The profession of arms in a democracy is not exempt from oversight or from consideration of just conduct, even in warfare. Where the will of the people, the moral high ground, and the technological high ground are the same, the profession will remain a useful and lofty one. If, however, the moral high ground is lost, a domino effect occurs: public support is lost, the technological high ground is lost, and the armed forces are lost.

Information warfare is hostile activity directed against any part of the knowledge and belief systems of an adversary. The 'adversary' is anyone uncooperative with the aims of the leader. Externally, this is the agreed upon 'enemy,' or the 'not us.' Internally, the adversary might be the traitor, the faint of heart, or the fellow traveler – anyone who opposes or is insufficiently cooperative with the leader who controls the means of information warfare. If the internal members of a group are insufficiently supportive of the aims of the leader during warfare, internal information warfare (including such things as propaganda, deception, character assassination, rumors, and lies) can be used

200. DiNardo, R.L. and Hughes, Daniel. "Some Cautionary Thoughts On Information Warfare." *Airpower Journal*, Winter 1995. EPI223

in attempts to make them more supportive of the aims of the leadership."201

Information war also involves hacking into the systems of adversaries such as often happens around the world. "As widely reported last week, the violence raging between Israelis and Palestinians has infected the Internet, as computer hackers on both sides of the conflict have launched sophisticated attacks on opponents' Web sites originating in the region. This week it was the American-Israel Public Affairs Committee's turn. On Wednesday afternoon, a group calling itself the Pakistani Hackerz Club seized control of the Web site belonging to the powerful pro-Israel lobby and replaced its home page with one containing anti-Israel slurs." 202

The problem with these kinds of attacks is that they restrict the flow of information and silence real debate of very different ideas and issues. It is now possible to develop a large base of knowledge from culling the internet in order to come to conclusions about political issues, economic decisions, medical choices and virtually any other area of interest to individuals.

The Air Intelligence Agency (AIA) is concerned about even the electromagnetic emanations which come from all computers. These energy fields can be measured and interpreted by adversaries with advanced technical knowledge. This is the very same technology used by law enforcement in combination with other innovations to monitor the activities of those who they wish to observe. "Perimeter Protection. The prime objective of the TEMPEST program is to control or contain any information bearing electromagnetic emanations coming from any information processor within an AIA facility." 203 TEMPEST is just one of the many initiatives in this area.

The heart of information warfare is in deception and manipulation. In reviews of military writings and other published

201. Szafranski, Col. Richard (USAF). "A Theory of Information Warfare: Preparing For 2020." *Air Chronicles* EPI232

202. Lancaster, John. "Abroad at Home." *washingtonpost.com*, Nov. 3, 2000. EPI2835

203 Dept. of the Air Force, HQ Air Intelligence Agency. "The Air Intelligence Agency Tempest And Emission Security Program." Air Intelligence Instruction 33-203. Aug. 22, 2000. EPI3745

materials the line between clearly identifiable adversaries is lost. The ability to monitor, without detection, the communications of private persons is a great temptation which is violated often. The ability to gain increasing amounts of information on each individual participant in modern society is unbelievable and incredibly invasive. Where will the lines be drawn, and what safeguards will be instituted, to protect the privacy rights of law-abiding citizens? The old line of "if you don't have anything to hide, why worry" has never been a good reason to invade one's home or communications and has a chilling effect on freedom and liberty.

Dominance of the Information Flow

Scientific knowledge is the real power behind modern governments. Science in many respects has become an elite club with its own language and traditions. The access to scientific knowledge has been critical to the explosion of our economies and private sector developments. Access to knowledge is now shifting away from the general population because of the development of "an entirely new, scientists-only computer network called vBNS that will exchange data at speeds that will blow away the worldwide wait of the Internet. Top speed of the vBNS, or 'very high speed Backbone Network System,' is more than 21,000 times faster than the average modem. 204 This is an incredible speed. When one considers this book as an example of information research, to have had the use of such a system would have increased the density of information collected many orders of magnitude beyond what has been done and it would have been completed in a fraction of the time. Perhaps someday we might all have access to this kind of information and use it for purposes that truly serve mankind by being accessible to the scrutiny of a vigilant public.

Counter Intelligence – Another Race

"A draft resolution calling for the United Nations to study the impact of information technologies on global security may force the Defense Department to consider international controls on the development and use of strategic information war-

204. Kelley, Matt. "Scientists sidestep Net's worldwide wait." *Anchorage Daily News*, Feb. 9, 1997. EPI346

fare tools....'We cannot permit the emergence of a fundamentally new area of international confrontation which may lead to an escalation of the arms race.'"205 Wake-up UN, the race is already on and for the United States and other modern governments the race is already being won. The international community is not going to stop or even slow the information race or the advances taking place in technology. Information technol-ogy is as critical to future economic growth and human advancement just as much as it represents a threat to global security. The issue should not be to stop what cannot be stopped but, rather, to create accountability to stop the abuse and unethical intrusions of governments, corporations and individuals.

The threat presented in this area is well understood by our potential adversaries: "statements from officials in mainland China, Russia and an unnamed third country to illustrate the power and the import of information warfare in the decades ahead. 'An adversary wishing to destroy the United States only has to mess up the computer systems of its banks by high technology means,' Tenet quoted an article in Beijing's official People's Liberation Daily as saying."206 This is where we are really exposed to abuse, all of which could easily be blamed on a hacker, other government or some third party when the real information intruder could be our own government. The information race is well engaged – let us all hope that another important race begins – the race for ethics, morality and the human high-ground of information technology.

Taiwan has been a source of intelligence in evaluating the threats posed by a modern China. The use of direct attack of information systems being one of the primary 'preemptive" methods for shutting down an enemy's war fighting capacity even before a conflict begins. "Air Force Lt. Gen. Abe C. Lin, director of the Defense Ministry information and Electronic Warfare Directorate, said in an interview with *The Washington Times* that the People's Republic of China is developing a variety of information warfare and electronic combat weapons in preparation

205. Verton, Daniel. "DOD faces infowar controls." *Federal Computer Week*, Jan. 11, 1999. EPI1159

206. Wolf, Jim. "CIA says US computer networks a target." *China Post*, July 30, 1998. EPI686

for a conflict with the Republic of China – also known as Taiwan." 207

"'Right now, the Net is like a street with a camera on every corner. Everything you do leaves a trace,'....Law enforcement agencies, employers and hackers can easily monitor e-mail and online chat; corporate Web sites gather information on visitors, then resell it to marketing companies,"208 and this is just the beginning.

Information warfare is here now and will continue to evolve at an ever quickening pace. The safeguards to the public will only be assured when the public insists and governments establish laws which they enforce to assure the free flow of information and the protection of privacy as well as national interests.

---

207 Gertz, Bill. *(Washington Times)*. "High-Tech Warfare." July 22, 2001. *washingtontimes.com* EPI3483

208. Beiser, Vince. "Hiding Web trails." *Maclean's*, Aug. 16, 1999. EPI1147

Chapter 5

Diverse Technology In the 21st Century

This section was written to knit together a number of technologies which will impact basic human rights, personal privacy and numerous other areas. It is our hope that this section will stimulate some debate of these issues with the expectation that this will facilitate the development of sound public policy in these areas.

In the context of this writing the issue of what technologies are right to use on people is discussed. It is important to look at the impact of these technologies in light of the accepted international standards of what is unreasonable in terms of physiological or physical torture. The "Convention against Torture and Other Cruel, Inhuman or Degrading Treatment or Punishment. Part I, Article I" provides a definition which can be used as a guide for assessing new technologies in terms of their use in civilian and military actions. The cruel reality is that torture is used throughout the world and the United States is one of the biggest exporters of devices used for this purpose in countries which are known perpetrators of torture. This was noted in our earlier work *Earth Rising – The Revolution.* The definition is as follows:

> "For the purposes of this Convention, the term 'torture' means any act by which severe pain or suffering, whether physical or mental, is intentionally inflicted on a person for such purposes as obtaining from him or a third person information or a confession, punishing him for an act he or a third person committed or is suspected of having committed, or intimidating or coercing him or a third person, or for any reason based on discrimination of any kind. When such pain or suffering by or at the instigation

of or with the acquiescence of a public official or other person acting in an official capacity. It does not include pain or suffering arising only from, inherent in or incidental to lawful sanctions."209

"The human rights group Amnesty International on Monday called for a ban on the global sales of American-made weapons and other equipment used to torture people. More than 80 American companies – manufacturers of high-voltage electroshock devices such as stun guns and restraints – have sold equipment over the last decade that in some instances were used for torture, according to a 56-page Amnesty report, 'Stopping the Torture Trade.'" 210

Nanotechnology Revisited

"The first motors made of DNA, the vehicle of inheritance, are unveiled today by an Anglo-American team of scientists. The DNA motors, which resemble tweezers closing and opening, are 100,000 times smaller than the head of a pin. The techniques used to make them may pave the way to electronic circuits 1,000 times more powerful than today's silicon chips, says the team at Bell Labs and the University of Oxford. The motors are self-sufficient and do not require other chemicals to operate." 211

"IBM physicists announced a breakthrough today that demonstrates atomic-scale circuitry – millions of times smaller that today's microprocessors – is feasible, and may eventually render modern electronic circuitry obsolete. If futurists prove correct, this nanotechnology will ultimately pack the power of a supercomputer into a device so small that they could be woven into garments powered by body heat, or injected into a person's bloodstream as super-intelligent diagnostic probes." 212

209. Government of the United States of America. Declaration and reservations made by the United States upon signature of the "Convention against Torture and Other Cruel, Inhuman or Degrading Treatment or Punishment." EPI1134

210 Delavigne, Moina. *(Cox News Service)*. "Rights group urges sales ban on torture weapons." *Miami Herald*, Feb. 27, 2001. EPI3183

211 Highfield, Roger. "Anglo-US scientists unveil tiny motors made out of DNA." *www.telegrapg.co.uk*, Aug. 10, 2000. EPI2558

212 Piller, Charles. "A Glimpse of Atomic-Scale Computing." *Latimes.com*, Feb. 3, 2000. EPI1379

"Well, miniaturization is another exponential trend in technology, and right now we're shrinking the size of technology by a factor of 5.6 per linear dimension per decade.Because it's self-replicating, nanotechnology will ultimately be able to provide anything in the physical world that we want, so if properly applied, it can meet all our needs and desires and create fantastic wealth. But there are also enormous dangers to nanotechnology. Self-replication run amok would be a nonbiological cancer that would be even more destructive than a biological cancer." 213

This is one of the complementary sciences which moves these advances forward where only the imagination of people seem to be the limiting factor. The idea of copying what nature does, from manipulation of genetic material to the control of complete environmental systems, is now possible for mankind. Should these technologies be allowed to advance without public disclosure and discussion of their implications for us all? How should science proceed when we now have the power to destroy everything that is valued by anyone?

Electromagnetic Pulse – The Attack on Electronics

We have explored this area in most of our past writing predicting the advancement of this technology first in 1993. The idea of using a surge of energy to override computers, weapon control systems or even vehicle ignitions has been the subject of intense research by the United States and others. The use of such systems have been developing and, as I write these words on January 21, 2003, CNN is reporting a BBC story where they suggest that the United States has perfected a system which they describe as artificial bolts of lighting – this is the essence of electromagnetic pulse weapons (EMP). "Congress became so disturbed by those first studies that it mandated creation of a new blue-ribbon panel, whose members Secretary of Defense Rumsfeld soon will select, to study US vulnerability to EMP attack. Russia's work in this area has been the best in the world, most experts agree. Russia has the best physicists in the world when it comes to RF weapons and EMP, says Barry Crane, a physicist and former F-4 pilot now working at the Institute for Defense Analysis who has visited Russia's top EMP laboratories

213 *Technology Review.* "The Story of the 21st Century." January-February 2000. EPI1427

and design bureaus. 'Many of their best EMP specialists are now working on contract in Communist China,' Crane tells *Insight*." 214 These systems are even being built in backyard experiments leading many to conclude that the risk of significant problems is great in this area.

"Two homemade weapons capable of frying electronics and crashing computers have been demonstrated at the US Army's Aberdeen Proving ground in Maryland. The tests were requested by the US government, to determine whether cheap but effective radio wave weapons could be made with little technical know-how." 215

Some are even suggesting that these attacks have already been engaged and are underway. "Cyberwar attack of electro-magnetic type against electronic/computer installation, is intended to cause denial of service for short or long periods of time. Some reports from Europe and the US suggest that IT electromagnetic attack is beginning to occur.

Most military programs are classified and the general public knows little concerning their nature but as the technology becomes available to criminals and terrorists, it may be directly applied to the infrastructure elements of our society. This includes financial institutions, aircraft, security, medical, automotive and other equipment used everyday in our society.

An important criteria for a cyber-terrorist would be that any of the parts and materials used would have to be those that could be easily found in any city and were not traceable by conventional counter-terrorist agencies such as the local police and insurance investigators.

From unclassified sources, we know that a lot of nations are well ahead in this field. With the size of a small briefcase, the generator could be placed very close to target system, like a computer at a desk. 1995 saw the first known use of HPM technology by subversives. Chechnyan rebels used HPM to defeat a Russian security system and gain access to a controlled

214 Timmerman, Kenneth. "US Threatened With EMP Attack." *Insightmag.com*, May 7, 2001. EPI3284

215 *Newscientist.com*. "Wave of destruction: Home-made radio frequency weapon fries electronics in US Army tests." May 3, 2001. EPI3279

area."216 HPM (High Power Microwave) is another way of creating the same effect and, as has been shown by others, is not difficult to produce. These systems can be constructed in a manner that is not damaging to an otherwise low-tech enemy because they do not rely on electronics as much as sophisticated economies or modern militaries. Technically backward advarsaries are not impacted in the same ways as modern states.

United States intelligence agencies are well aware of the threat. Weapons laboratories are creating these weapons while they are also working on counter measures as well as shielding materials that can protect US systems. We are a long way from such protections being spread to the public although they offer great potential. In our discussion of the dangers of cell phones this could be a place for civilian use for example. The idea that some of the electromagnetic sources of health damaging emissions could be shielded and rendered significantly safer for the public should be explored as a priority.

Europe's View of Emerging Technologies

We have had great opportunities to work with European legislators, researchers and media in trying to bring many of these issues forward. Our earlier work was intended to bring awareness prior to the kind of events that would likely accelerate the pace of these innovations without public review. Since the events of September 11, 2001 the pace has quickened and a chill has been cast over those who attempt to expose abuse while balancing national interests. Our approach has been to limit that which we report to only those matters that are part of the public record. We have also been careful to avoid any detailed information on how these devices are constructed. As a result of recent events it is even more apparent that public discussion is required.

The European perspective on these matters is interesting in that they appear much more willing to deal with these issues in the "clear light of day." We are including below lengthy direct quotes from the public record to illustrate the European perspective as well as their concerns. Americans, as we become

216 EME AB, Swedish Defence Research Agency (FOI). "Electromagnetic terrorism or High Power Microwave HPM-weapons." www.eme.se/Summary_in_English.html EPI3295

aware of these issues increasingly follow the same line of alarm and a desire for debate. A recent study brings these issues alive below:

> "The study questions the wisdom of maintaining the status quo where government and company research, often undertaken after chemical irritant weapons have been authorized, continues as the main approach to justifying alleged harmlessness. Given that different countries even within the EU have adopted different stances, there is a risk of not having proper regard to health and safety concerns, since many problems with toxic chemicals only emerge many years after operational usage. Both citizens and officers could have a future legal claim if scientific assertions of safety were later found to be less well informed or negligent. An alternative option would be to further consider the options outlined in a previous STOA report which suggested that all EU Member States should establish the following principles: Research on chemical irritants should be published in open scientific journals before authorization for any usage is permitted and that the safety criteria for such chemicals should be treated as if they were drugs rather than riot control agents; Research on the alleged safety of existing crowd control weapons and of all future innovations in crowd control weapons should be placed in the public domain prior to any decision towards deployment...
>
> The European Union is advised to give consideration to taking up the formal request of the British government made on 28th July, 1997, which asked all of the member States to follow their example in taking the necessary measure[s] to prevent the export or transshipment of portable devices designed or modified for riot or control purposes or self-protection to administer an electric shock, including electroshock batons, electroshock shields, stun guns, and tasers, and specially designed components for such devices...
>
> The report warns against adopting ever more powerful crowd control weapons as technical fixes and allowing the policing assumptions of the United States to organize, militarize and market public order options for the

European Union without public debate or accountability. Questions over the reliability and safety of certain US crowd policing weapons and practices should urge caution. Technical data in regard to the 2nd generation of crowd control weapons from the US are discussed in this report, which advises that they should not be taken at face value. All such weapons should be subject to independent testing and licensing control and until and unless such a checking regime is in place, a moratorium should be considered on accepting any of this technology into European military and police crowd control arsenals. This would mean that no US made or licensed 2nd generation chemical irritant, kinetic, acoustic, laser, electromagnetic frequency, capture, entanglement, injector or electrical disabling and paralyzing, should be deployed within Europe unless legally binding guarantees are forthcoming from the agencies deploying these weapons about their alleged safety.

The military police industrial complex has spawned an ever growing arsenal of new crowd control weapons offering the dubious promise of even more powerful technical fixes for social and political problems. In practical terms since the main seat of innovation in this area is the United States, this would let an alien American policing culture set the public order agenda in Europe. It would also entail a wealth of unwelcome impacts, including escalation of conflict and a loosening of community support for the police. More socially sensitive alternatives need to be found but there are obvious dangers in substituting one technical fix for another.

The report questions whether CCTV cameras could be used throughout European cities to provide a chill effect to dissuade potential rioters from creating civil disturbances as a substitute for crowd control weapons. (The approach is based on algorithmic face recognition systems linked into these networks that could then be used to track down and target malfactors). The problem with this option is that it does not enable any real time intervention to further contain trouble as it is breaking out. Experience in those countries which already have mass city centre surveillance, such as the UK, is that they adopt both CCTV and public order tactics and technologies, not either/or. Trouble-makers have learnt to mask their face and operate outside of the camera's reach. The other danger here is of course in creating a network of mass supervision which may be used for very different purposes to those for which it was originally intended. To effectively deploy these systems would mean putting the whole of society under continuous surveillance which would be assuming a continuing benign level of political stability which rarely exists in the long term, not even in Europe.

That deployment of OC (pepper-gas) should be halted across the EU until independent research has more fully evaluated any risks it poses to health. A further precautionary measure would be to ask Member States to tag the health records of all those affected by the spray who seek medical treatment, in case common health problems emerge in the future.

The Status quo option could be maintained which allows potentially lethal crowd control weapons to be used on our streets which because of their inaccuracy could be targeted onto innocent bystanders, children etc. However, no European State has the death penalty for public order offenses.

New legal limits, as suggested by the Patten Commission in Northern Ireland, should restrict inherently unsafe technology which because of its technical and design characteristics is potentially lethal in many of the operational circumstances where it might realistically be deployed. Any Kinetic Impact Weapons with an energy greater than 122 joules should be considered as a lethal firearm and their use should be regarded as illegal if the use of lethal firearms in the same context would be illegal. For example, where innocent bystanders may become unwitting targets. In this context, steps should be taken to ensure that all Kinetic Energy munitions are ballistically traceable to the weapon and security unit.

Whilst allegedly non-lethal crowd control weapons have gained increasing prominence in recent years as tools for managing contemporary internal security demands, there has been a long-standing search for, and deployment of, such weapons throughout the 20th Century dating from their use in the former European colonies. Historic examples include so-called tear gas, wooden and rubber bullets, electric cattle prods and watercannons used by British colonial forces in Cyprus and Hong Kong, who also developed a new set of riot control techniques. The earlier STOA report on this subject emphasized that new crowd control technologies encompassed not just the hardware or apparatus of technical performance, but also the software – the standard operating procedures, routines, skills and associated tactics for deploying public crowd control weapons. Thus these riot control tactics themselves can be considered as a technology, capable of refinement and transfer and consisting of a spectrum of options containing increasing levels of coercion. Many of these riot control techniques have been further systematized in terms of collective tactics e.g. using wedges, shields, batons, horses and riot weapons which work on a formulaic basis according to the military model which spawned them. It is now widely recognized that this process can militarize the police into Special Weapons and Tactics Units such as the Grenz Shutz Gruppe in Germany, the Gendarmeries in France, the Caribiniere in Italy; the Special Patrol and Tactical Aid Groups in the UK and the FBI, DEA and BATF paramilitary teams in the USA. Such groups undertake tactical training that is the mirror image of their military counterparts involved in operations other than war and adopt the same weapons technologies. The perceived utility of this class of technology derives from the flexibility it supposedly offers states in their use of force during public order operations, whether organized by the police, military or another force in between.

The current market in crowd control weapons covers everything from basic truncheons; side-handle batons; riot shields; kinetic impact weapons such as rubber and PVC plastic baton rounds; single and multi-shot riot guns; water cannons which have been enhanced to fire slugs or bullets of water, marker dye and a range of chemical irritants for punishing demonstrators; stun grenades; a wide variety of chemical irritant grenades; tear gas projectiles; aerosols; and bulk sprayers (yet all based primarily on 5 disabling chemicals namely CS, CN, CR, OC and Pava); a range of electroshock weapons including 50,000 volt riot shields and hand held shock batons varying from 50,000 to 400,000 volts.

Disabling chemical weapons used for law enforcement consist of a disabling chemical and a dispersion mechanism. There are inherent difficulties inevitable in marrying a chemical which has high effectiveness at very low doses with the requirement of low toxicity. Intensive work began in the 1950s, particularly in the USA and the UK, who shared their information on Chemical & Biological Weapons (CBW). In 1956, the UK War Office established the need for a chemical weapon able to drive back fanatical rioters which led to the adoption of CS, (then code numbered T792) for use in the colonies of Cyprus and British Guyana. In 1958, a Task Group on CBW was set up in the USA. The US Chemical Corps recommended two CW agents for consideration, namely CS and the vomiting agent DM, whilst describing mustard gas as primarily a non-lethal agent. Work also began on searching for chemical incapacitates particularly non-lethal persistent chemical agents that are capable of attacking through the skin and can produce incapacitation for one to three weeks. Nowadays, the Chemical Weapons Convention permits the use of tear gas and other toxic temporarily disabling chemicals and their precursors for law enforcement and domestic riot control purposes (which it does not define) as long as the chemicals listed in Schedule 1 of the convention are not used. This provision rules out DM, which is a toxic arsenic based substance previously held by certain countries outside the EU, including South Africa, which secretly explored the use of MDMA (Ecstasy) as a crowd control incapacitant.

It should be remembered that the US for the purposes of the Chemical Weapons Convention (CWC) has a different set of definitions on what is permissible and what is excluded for riot control under the general purpose of the convention. Under Executive order 11850 of April 1974, four examples are given where the US can use riot control agents, namely; (a) in riot control situations under direct and distinct US military control, to control rioting prisoners of war; (b) in situations which civilians are used to mask or screen attacks and civilian casualties can be reduced or avoided; (c) in rescue missions in remote isolated areas, of downed aircrews and passengers and escaping prisoners and (d) in rear echelon areas outside the zone of immediate combat to protect convoys from civil disturbances, terrorists and para-military organizations. It does not take much imagination, given the failure of the CWC to define domestic riot control and law enforcement, that in operations other than war, such as peacekeeping missions, the US might feel it was legitimate to deploy new agents and dissemination systems. By 1991 the US Army said they now had a device which could deliver a potent riot control compound. They advised a class of compounds has been selected and viable analogues are under evaluation for acceptability in meeting initial generic requirements. It is likely that these agents are part of the fentanyl family. In operational circumstances, it is very difficult to control levels of individual intake and one person's sleeping draft would be another's lethal dose. Used in conjunction with lethal weapons or where a crowd was fleeing, additional fatalities could occur from either falling or crush injuries or simply being a sitting target for a nervous recruit expecting the worst. The war in the former Yugoslavia has shown how men engaged in ethnic conflicts use mass rape as a weapon and immobilizing chemicals could easily form an adjunct to such policies but one which few commanders will ever admit.

Directed Energy Weapons – These weapons have created the most heated debate. Some variants such as isotropic radiators have come into the markets as omni-directional laser bright rounds, where precision targeting is impossible. They are being promoted as cheap dazzle devices against people and optics but little has emerged in the way of technical data. Other more directional lasers have been used as dazzle devices, for example the USAF

Saber 203 laser dazzle system, prototypes of which were used by the US marines in Somalia. Blinding laser weapons are banned by the Blinding Laser Convention. Nevertheless, even after this treaty, their use is still being promoted for law enforcement. A recent development has been using a UV laser which can ionize the air sufficiently for it to conduct an electric charge. This enables an electric shock to be delivered over some distance to create muscle paralysis or tetanization. A fully working prototype is still some way off but the principle has been successfully tested using a Lumonics Hyper-X 400 excimer laser at the University of California at San Diego. Other directed energy weapons are being explored. For example in 1997, Edward Scannel of the US Army Laboratory identified a Vortex Ring Gun which is a combustion Ring Gun creating vortices for impulse or chemical delivery and a range of high powered acoustic technology. The literature talks of acoustic bullets, beams and blastwave projectors. Comments on acoustic weapons have suggested they can be tunable, radiating a directed energy beam of 90-120 decibels to provide anything from extreme levels of annoyance and distraction through to 140-150 decibels for strong physical bodily damage to tissues, to shock-wave levels of more than 170 decibels, producing instantaneous blastwave trauma which could be lethal.

The current leader in acoustic technology in the US is a small company in Huntington Beach, California called Scientific Applications and Research Associates which is reported to have made vortices which are capable of providing an area denial function. However, despite the claims of powerful infra-sound weapons capable of making people sick and causing involuntary defecation, a presentation by Jurgen Altman of the University of Dortmund at the 1999 Janes conference, Fielding Weapons for the New Millennium said such claims were based on Physics not as we know it. In a more detailed technical study Altman provides a tightly argued case for doubting the technical workability of such weapons over longer distances. At shorter distances with explosive driven strong sound blast waves there would be a case for including such weapons within the SLrUS criteria of banning weapons which target a particular aspect of human anatomy. The most controversial non-lethal crowd control and anti-materiel technology proposed by the US are so called Radio Frequency or Directed Energy weapons that can allegedly manipulate human behavior in a variety of unusual ways. Some microwave systems have been proposed which can raise body temperature to between 105 to 107 degrees F, to provide a disabling effect in a manner based on the microwave cooker principle. However, the greatest concern is with systems which can directly interact with the human nervous system. There are many reports on so called psychotronic weapons which are beyond the brief of this study but one comment can be made. The research undertaken to date in the US and Russia can be divided into two related areas: (i) individual mind control and (ii) crowd control. That the US has undertaken a variety of mind control programmes in the past such as MkULTRA and MkDELTA is a matter of public record and those using electromagnetic radiation such as PANDORA have been the focus of researchers in para-politics for many years. More recently, authors such as Begich and Roderick have alleged significant breakthroughs in the ability of military high frequency electromagnetic technologies to manipulate human behavior. What is admitted by the military authorities in the US is that research programmes using so-called directed energy weapons for anti-personnel and anti-materiel purposes are proceeding into prototype stages. The military utility of these weapons is that they provide a tunable or rheostat ability, a need that is emerging as part of the new US military intervention doctrine of so called layered defense. This means in practice an onion style of risk where anyone coming into contact with the outer shell may be sickened, paralyzed. Entering subsequent levels may lead to being physically harmed, disabled or permanently maimed whilst the core of the zone is protected by lethal technology, contact with which is fatal.

Universal Declaration On Human Genome & Human Rights & Genetic Weapons. Human genome research is an area of rapid innovation and scientific development is making potentially awesome capabilities available to the State to manipulate and manage human crowd behavior. A good case in point is the Human Genome Project and the Human Diversity Project which have the potential to release race specific control functions and to create weapons which induce heightened levels of anxiety and submission. International agreements are already in place which attempt to prevent the abuse of such innovations e.g. the Universal Declaration on the Genome and Human Rights, adopted by UNSEEN on November 11, 1997. Such legislation needs to be more effective particularly in guarding against the import of relatively alien US concepts of crowd domination and control (using technologies which have been literally dreamt up in their national atomic laboratories). European democratic traditions are quite different. Options and mechanisms are presented above which would make such legislation more effective in regard to regulating the appropriate usage of crowd control weapons and further restricting any abuse of such systems in creating gross human rights violations.

Designer Bio-Weapons For Selective Mass Control. The rapid change in biotechnology, including genetic engineering, is already revolutionizing medicine and agriculture. However relatively little attention has been paid to its potential malign use as surgically tractable future technologies of political control. This possibility of a malign breakthrough was recognized in the early nineties when important advances in the Human Genome Project (involving the mapping of some 3 billion pairs of human DNA) and the Human Diversity Project (which looked at the genetic basis for racial differences) were already taking place. Whilst the idea of genetic weapons is not new, it was previously thought such targeting was impossible because humans are so similar genetically. However the Genome Diversity Project which stores genetic material from 500 populations around the world has found significant differences in blood group proteins. These differences are now thought to be sufficiently stable and large to be targeted either by using genetically modified organisms or toxins which select a particular genetic marker. Given the heterogeneous nature of many populations including those of the US, only certain political areas and borders could be targeted without the risk of so called friendly fire. The biotechnology revolution will bring enormous benefits to our understanding and our ability to intervene in life processes. Many commercial activities will be transformed by research such as tailor-making drugs more exactly for human receptor sites known to be linked to particular metabolic pathways. One indicator of the awesome rate of change in this area is the meteoric rise in the number of patent requests filed at the US Patent and Trademark Office for nuclei acid sequences: 4,000 in 1991 and 500,000 in 1996. Multinational drug companies are currently doing a complete survey of each of the constituent nucleotides for each human genome group. A major driving force is thwarting cancer: some genes force cell growth, some genes inhibit cell growth. The Holy Grail of this research is to find a biochemical tool which can enter cancer cells, correct cell growth then stop. However, the mirror image of this research is that it will yield knowledge on how to go the other way. As the data on human receptor sites accumulates, the risk of breakthroughs in malign targeting of suitable micro-organisms at either cell membrane level, or via viral vectors, grows correspondingly. The development of such genetic based weapons is currently banned under the 1972 Biological & Toxin Weapons Convention (BTWC), the 1925 Geneva Protocols and the 1948 Genocide Convention. Alas, unlike the CWC, there are currently no verification procedures for the BTWC, it is a gentleman's agreement. The emergence of pepper-gas as a weapon for crowd control is a case in point – as a plant toxin it is covered by the BTWC but has simply slipped through the net in terms of internal security operations. Other natural and synthetic toxins used for such purposes may be even more hazardous, particularly if they are reengineered. Already the properties of saxitoxin, banned under the CWC and the bio-regulator endthelia (which is a very powerful constrictor of blood vessels and can produce aneurysms) have been noted. The potential for malign applications emerging for semi-lethal crowd control from this research should not be dismissed. Arguably there should be a set of new norms regarding the use of such momentous knowledge of life processes for human manipulation and control. The issue is too complex to be adequately covered by this study but the potential significance of developments in biotechnology leading to a third generation of instruments to manipulate human behavior deserves a specialist study in its own right. If such a study could be completed in time for the BTWC 2001 review conference, it could help produce a greater scientific knowledge of these issues and gain further support for strengthening the convention.

Other critics say that the notion of soft-kill is a fallacy. The Nobel prize winning scientific organization Pugwash, has come to the conclusion that the term non-lethal should be abandoned, not only because it covers a wide variety of different weapons but also because it can be dangerously misleading. In combat situations, sub-lethal weapons are likely to be used in coordination with other weapons and could increase overall lethality. Weapons purportedly developed for conventional military or peacekeeping use are also likely to be used in civil wars or for oppression by brutal governments. Weapons developed for police use may encourage the militarization of police forces or be used for torture. If a generic term is needed, less-lethal or pre-lethal might be preferable. The reality can indeed be far from non-lethal. A current and future domain of this weaponry is during internal security operations, where it provides authoritarian regimes with new tools for crushing dissent. Already variants of less-lethal paralyzing and incapacitating electroshock weapons have found a role in torture. The new weapons potentially offer the torturing states a spine chilling arsenal of repressive instruments. Whilst the genie of advanced crowd control weapons may not go back into the bottle, there is still time for the European Union to develop consistent and appropriate structures of accountability. Pugwash considered that each of the emerging less-lethal weapons technologies required urgent examination and that their development or adoption should be subject to public review. The process should be transparent, adaptable and open to public and political

> scrutiny. Any class of technology shown to be excessively injurious, cruel, inhumane or indiscriminate, should be either prohibited or subject to stringent and democratic controls." 217

Non-Lethals Weapons?

These new weapons are theoretically more humane than just outright killing but there is a lot of confusion surrounding these systems. One of the major issues is in the names themselves, "non-lethal" and "less-than-lethal" weapons. The names imply that these new systems are temporary, not deadly, while reality shows a much different picture. Incapacitating gas has been one of the areas of controversy as has been pointed out by researchers for years. Gas can cause respiratory distress leading to death, and has on many occasions. The most dramatic example was in late 2002 when Russian forces used gas to dislodge Chechnyan rebels from a theater in Moscow resulting in over a hundred deaths, mostly civilian hostages.

The definition of a non-lethal weapon has drawn the attention of several people and resulted in some bizarre assertions. The most insane and foolish definition put forward, in our opinion, was made by Dr. Edward Teller, one of the world's advocates for nukes and atomic weapons. He shares a much different view:

> "Not everyone, of course, has the same idea of what 'non-lethal' means. At a conference on non-lethal weapons held near Washington D.C., last November, Edward Teller described mini-nukes, used to bombard enemy territory and destroy roads, bridges, and communication systems, as non-lethal (*New Scientist*, December 11, 1993). Teller told the conference that if civilian populations were warned before the bombs were dropped, 'a plan of this kind could work out without a single casualty.' Teller is eager to develop baby bombs, which he said, could be ready in three years at a cost of only a 'few hundred million dollars.'" 218

217 OMEGA Foundation (Author). "Crowd Control Technologies (An appraisal of technologies for political control). Publisher: European Parliament, The STOA Programme. June 2000. EPI2754

218 Rothstein, Linda. *(The Bulletin of the Atomic Scientists)*. "The 'soft-kill' solution." 1994. *www.bullatomsci.org* EPI3667

In preparing an opposition force for an eventual conflict with Iraq the United States began training in non-lethal techniques which included the use of quite lethal systems. Why mislead the public in these areas? Why not acknowledge the reality of what is really being done? "The training of the first group of members from the London based Iraqi National Congress will begin next month in a military facility in College Station, Texas. The five-day course will provide instruction on such weapons as the semi-automatic Kalishnikov, 12-gauge shotgun and other firearms.

US officials said the Bush administration has not changed previous policy and termed the course as non-lethal." 219

Another definition and perhaps a more complete definition was put forward by the Department of Defense in 1996:

"SUBJECT: Policy for Non-Lethal Weapons.

...C.DEFINITION. Non-Lethal Weapons that are explicitly designed and primarily employed so as to incapacitate personnel or material, while minimizing fatalities, permanent injury to personnel, and undesired damage to property and the environment.

1. Unlike conventional lethal weapons that destroy their targets principally through blast, penetration and fragmentation, non-lethal weapons employ means other than gross physical destruction to prevent the target from functioning.

2. Non-lethal weapons are intended to have one, or both of the following characteristics:

a. They have relatively reversible effects on personnel or material.

b. They affect objects differently within their area of influence.

D. POLICY

It is DoD policy that:

1. Non-lethal weapons, doctrine, and concepts of operation shall be designed to reinforce deterrence and expand the range of

219 *World Tribune.com.* "Special Forces begins 'non-lethal' weapons training for Iraqi opposition." Feb. 15, 2001. EPI3187

options available to commanders.
2. Non-lethal weapons should enhance the capability of US forces to accomplish the following objectives:

a. Discourage, delay, or prevent hostile actions.

b. Limit escalation.

c. Take military action in situations where use of lethal force is not the preferred option.

d. Better protect our forces.

e. Temporarily disable equipment, facilities and personnel.

3. Non-lethal weapons should also be designed to help decrease the post-conflict costs of reconstruction.

4. The availability of non-lethal weapons shall not limit a commander's inherent authority and obligation to use all necessary means available and to take all appropriate action in self-defense.

5. Neither the presence nor the potential effect of non-lethal weapons shall constitute an obligation for their employment or a higher standard for employment of force than provided for by applicable law. In all cases, the United States retains the option for immediate use of lethal weapons, when appropriate, consistent with international law.

6. Non-lethal weapons shall not be required to have a zero probability of producing fatalities or permanent injuries. However, while complete avoidance of these effects is not guaranteed or expected, when properly employed, non-lethal weapons should significantly reduce them as compared with physically destroying the same target.

7. Non-lethal weapons may be used in conjunction with lethal weapon systems to enhance the latter's effectiveness and efficiency in military operations. This shall apply across the range of military operations to include those situations where overwhelming force is employed." 220

The idea that warfare can be nonlethal is not likely in the near or long term. "War is still the ground of death and life, the path of survival and destruction, and even the slightest innocence

220 Department of Defense Directive. July 9, 1996. Number 3000.3. Signed by John P. White, Deputy Secretary of Defense. EPI3128

is not tolerated. Even if someday all weapons have been made completely humane, a kinder war in which bloodshed may be avoided is still war. It may alter the cruel process of war, but there is no way to change the essence of war, which is one of compulsion, and therefore it cannot alter its cruel outcome, either."221 War is lethal and results in death. The use of any technology should be weighed with care to assure that it will be used in a way that lines up with human values in the context of military missions.

The United States Air Force is well aware of the risks and variables in using these kinds of systems yet neglects to include this information in their public pronouncements on these systems. "Because of biological variability there will always be uncertainty in predicting the biological responses to NLWs [Non Lethal Weapons]. Even among a consistent population of humans, such as a group of young adult males, there will be a variability in responses to the same stimulus. When the variance of the population increases, for example by adding persons of differing sizes, ages, weights, frailty, health, and both sexes, so will the variability of the population response to most NLWs."222 This point, raised by the military, is the heart of the difficulty in predicting outcomes – for one individual the effect is non-lethal for another person it is the opening volley leading to a funeral.

The United States has continued to establish and develop its programs and John Alexander continues to figure prominently in the promotion of these technologies. "Non-Lethal Defense III is designed as a response to the requirements articulated in Non-Lethal Defense II held 6-7 March 1996, in Arlington, Virginia. At that time senior defense and Law Enforcement officials discussed what they believed to be an urgent need for the research, development, and acquisition of new non-lethal weapons. Since then, the US Department of Defense has formalized the Non-Lethal Weapons Program and created the Joint Non-Lethal

221 Liang et al. *Assumptions on War and Tactics in the Age of Globalization,* Feb. 1999, Beijing. People's Liberation Army Literature Arts Publishing House. Central Intelligence Agency, Oct. 1999. Approved for release May 2001. Obtained by Harlan Girard through Freedom of Information Act request. EPI3533

222 Murphy, Michael R. PhD. Directed Energy Bioeffects Division, Human Effectiveness Directorate. Air Force Research Laboratory, Brooks Air Force Base. "Biological Effects of Non-Lethal Weapons: Issues and Solutions." 1997. EPI3874

Weapons Directorate to administer that program."223 These programs are used to bring people together around these themes. The programs are not all bad. Many of the evolving technologies could be very useful in policing and military actions. The need for open public discussion of the impacts of the technology requires more than limited access meetings followed by controlled press releases which is what is now taking place.

While in a rush to move forward, the biological effects are still being considered. "The response of biological systems exposed to Non-Lethal Weapons (NLW) is not well understood. The literature contains predominately anecdotal references to effects that have not been systematically studied and are subject to ambiguous interpretation. Without a clear understanding of the mechanisms by which the device effects couple to the target and evoke response modes of interest, there is no way to extrapolate the results of animal experiments to humans. In particular, for devices which radiate mechanical waves through the body, such as High Power Acoustic Beam Weapons, (HPAMWs), nonpenetrating projectiles, and toriodal [sic] vortices; differences between humans and animals with respect to tissue properties, organ and cavity geometry, elastic properties of connective tissue, and frequency response of specific anatomical structures, strongly suggest that there will not be an obvious correspondence between response modes evoked in animals and humans."

"Our approach analyzes conventional trauma databases to identify regions of the human body that may be susceptible to NLW effects and response thresholds that can evoke desired effects. Once the pathogenesis of a potential effect has been identified, experiments using insitu instrumentation and biosimulants configured to mimic relevant anatomic features are implemented. These experiments support development of analytical models that describe the physics of the interaction and which can ultimately be extrapolated to biological systems." 224 A good deal of this type of analysis has already been done and a number of new systems evolved as have been disclosed in this book and the others we have written.

223 Alexander, John. "Introduction To Non-Lethal Defense III Proceedings." Feb. 1998. EPI3174

224 Eisler, R.D. (Mission Research Corporation). "A Methodology Using Biosimulants to Describe Non-Lethal Weapon Effects on People." Non-Lethal Defense III, Feb. 1998. EPI3177

The Russian Center For Strategic and International Studies was even more clear on the implications of these weapons and new energy based systems. "In our experts' opinion, a combination of precision weapons more sophisticated than now, an information/control system as well as diverse kinds of nonlethal weapons (those developed and still under development) with precision means of delivery will lead to the creation of a powerful conventional weapon system which will become equivalent to nuclear weapons in terms of the capability of deterrence and destruction and will surpass them in terms of flexibility of use." 225

Taking the Issue to Europe

Over the years I have made ten trips to Europe on these and related issues in order to lobby for a change in the direction of these technologies. MEP Tom Spencer of the European Parliament and Chairman of the Foreign Affairs Committee at the time, was our great friend in bringing these issues into public debate. Over the objections of the United States he moved the issues forward to a hearing. I flew to Europe a few days before the hearing.

After a rush of short meetings on the issues my agenda was given to me for the evening. A dinner had been arranged the night before the public hearing with the Subcommittee members, two members of the European media and the others who would testify the next day. In that five hour meeting we discussed and demonstrated one of the technologies we were referencing. The committee members understood the issues and were prepared for the next day's hearings. NATO and the United States had rebuffed the European's request to produce someone for the hearing. The committee was incensed and expressed their discontent. I was given over an hour of extended time to present testimony as were the others assembled to debate the issues.

On February 5, 1998, MEP Tom Spencer, and members of his Foreign Affairs subcommittee, provided the hearing for HAARP and Non-lethal weapons. We had coordinated a strategy

225 Borisov et al. (Associates of the Russian Center For Strategic and International Studies). *Moscow Nezavisimoye Voyennoye Obozreniye*. "Wars Are Changing Their Look: The Growing Role of Nonlethal Weapons In Methods of Combat Operations." May 22-28, 1998. No. 19. Central Intelligence Agency, July 1998. Approved for release Jan. 2001. Obtained by Freedom of Information Act request by Harlan Girard. EPI3268

for this while together in the Black Sea in a conference some months before. In the hearing we openly challenged the reported deployment of non-lethal weapons and ionosphereic experimentation without clear policy frameworks. We had obtained a document called *Ionospheric Modification for Weapons Applications* which was produced as a non-classified document by NATO France. NATO had refused to appear for the hearing using the excuse that "they had no policy on nonlethal weapons or ionosphereic modification".

Later that year it was reported that. "Recently, the NATO Committee to develop policy for the employment of NLWs met in Washington. Mr. Charles Swett, the Chairman of the Committee, hosted the meeting which lasted for two days. This was the second in a set of meetings designed to provide NATO-assigned forces a broad framework within which they might employ non-lethal technologies. Col. Mazzara, the Director of the Joint NLW Programs, is the US Military Advisor to the committee which will meet again next month in the United Kingdom. A NATO policy for NLWs is anticipated next spring." 226 Their work continued when it was reported; "A Joint Non-Lethal Weapons Master Plan is in the process of being developed to provide program overview, direction, and guidance for the execution of the Joint Non-Lethal Weapons Program in support of Joint Vision 2010. It will be a tool for managing the implementation of the vision." 227

The European Parliament began to act in early 1999 with passage of a resolution in opposition to HAARP and some non-lethal weapons. They called for additional research and analysis of the existing body of research which has since been done. The European legislatures have moved much further and faster in the interests of human rights in these situations. The knowledge of these technologies is widespread and considered in the same vein as nukes, poison gas and blinding lasers. Not that some of the new systems shouldn't be used but careful considerations must be made in advance of use.

Our government continues to develop these programs while the public discussion evolves "after the fact" rather than in advance of use. Advance debate, before the expenditures are made,

226 *Joint NLW Directorate News*. "NATO Policy Committee Meets." Vol. 1 No. 7, Aug. 1998. EPI3088

227 Joint Non-Lethal Weapons Directorate. "JNLWP Master Plan." 3rd Quarter 1999, Vol. 2, Issue 3. EPI3091

would provide the public a chance to rule on the ethical merit of these technologies. The best examples of where these things go wrong, when this is not the case, are shown by the military's own record.

"During early FY99, the 66mm Vehicle-Launched Non-Lethal Grenades (VL NLG) Program suffered a setback. The program, which had been accelerated from a five-year to a three-year development effort, laid its hopes on modifying an existing L8 grenade design to achieve the stingball blunt trauma and the flash-bang payloads. During Engineering Design and Lethality Testing, the following discrepancies were discovered:

b) If the grenade was launched into a crowd, the large bursting charge required for reliable payload dispersion would likely result in permanent hearing loss. In addition, unexploded grenades could cause severe injury to the head, neck or torso..." 228

In a separate report, "The Joint Non-Lethal Weapons Directorate (JNLWD) commissioned Pennsylvania State University for the Human Effects Advisory Panel (HEAP). The mission of HEAP is to provide independent assessment of human effects issues surrounding non-lethal weapons. Their first tasking was to assess the current blunt trauma, human effect characterization methodology used by the services. The final report of the HEAP was delivered in March 1999. It raises a number of issues that warrant discussion within the services.

The first order of business was to quantitatively define 'non-lethal' in the context of non-lethal weapons. By this definition, a non-lethal weapon could potentially cause no effect in some fraction of the population, while causing permanent injury or death in another. This model is extremely useful in explaining the goal of the Joint Non-Lethal Weapons Program, but one should not use it as a go/no go test for the acceptability of any specific system.

The HEAP was critical of the services' methodologies for assessing injury from blunt impact munitions because the models used are not validated and do not address a

228 Joint Non-Lethal Weapons Directorate. "66mm Redesign Effort." 3rd Quarter 1999, Vol. 2, Issue 3. EPI3089

number of likely injury modes. In addition, none of the models used for blunt trauma address the concept of 'minimal non-lethal effect.' This information is critical for proper employment of these weapons." 229

The military has continued to develop these systems having built a strong foundation of knowledge. The idea of energy weapons, those that use energy rather than bullets and bomb fragments, forming the base of this technology is a far stretch from the sticky foam, nets and tasers being disclosed in press releases. This is beginning to change and will continue to change as more disclosures are made in the aftermath of September 11th and as we move toward the next conflict in the Middle East.

Beam Weapons

"The near future may see US military units employing beam weapons on the battlefield. Two Air Force Research Laboratory teams led the technology development. One team was the laboratory's directed energy directorate at Kirtland Air Force Base, N.M., and the other was from the human effectiveness directorate at Brooks AFB, Texas. Approximately $40 million has been spent on this technology over the past decade."230 In these programs perhaps only $40 million was spent but this represents only a fraction of the money that is being spent. A great deal had already been done and is being accomplished.

The US government continues to compartmentalize work in these areas. Compartmentalization is the idea of taking large programs and breaking them into smaller disassociated efforts so that the lefthand cannot see what the righthand is doing. This is the way projects are developed and security is maintained in their development. The United States and several other countries have used this approach since the Manhattan project, which eventually brought us the atom bomb.

Other governments use the opposite approach in developing their weapons systems. In this approach multidisciplinary teams are put together in order to see the fuller implications of research rather than separating the sciences and

229 Joint Non-Lethal Weapons Directorate. "HEAP – Blunt Impact Munitions." 3rd Quarter 1999, Vol. 2, Issue 3. EPI3090

230 *AFPN.* "Sci-fi beam weapons become reality in new nonlethal technology." March 2, 2001. EPI3157

their research teams. This provides the added benefit of a multidimensional view of the concepts and various types of impact that might otherwise be missed. This is what allowed, in part, the former Soviet Union to keep up with the U. S. technologically.

Floating the Trial Balloons

Another ploy used by the military is the limited release of information or "floating a trial balloon" as is often said in the United States. This is the idea of providing some information in order to test the public opposition or support of the idea. These lead to the same public opinion shaping methods employed by corporations for selling everything from automobiles to pharmaceuticals. The idea of motivating changes in public opinion are often the outcome as was seen in the Revolution in Military Affairs (RMA) often referred to by the military in the United States.

An example of the military's need to assess public opinion is illustrated by the following; "One of the problems in Military Operations in Urban Terrain (MOUT) is that the fighters and the non-combatants are intermixed. A potential solution is the use of directed energy weapons to temporarily incapacitate everyone in the target area. In order to gauge the public, media, and policy maker perception of these weapons, the JNLWD and the Marine Corps Warfighting Lab provided a demonstration on 19 Aug. 98 (1000–1530) at the Quantico Military Operations in Urban Terrain (MOUT) facility. Other non-lethal weapons were on display for viewing." 231 The disclosure is important and does provide some opportunity to get public opinion and regulate the developments accordingly. Unfortunately, often public opinion is discounted by the military and other "public" organizations and other agendas are followed. In the cases of weapon systems, under cover of national security laws, much is missed. While we acknowledge the need for the laws and the need to limit access to the construction of these technologies it is important to discuss more widely the concepts prior to development and use. At the present time we only see the use of the technology after the fact rather than the public having the opportunity to react to the uses of the technology prior to deployment or development in the first place. In a democracy, within a democratic republic, individuals

231 *Joint NLW Directorate News.* "Joint Non-Lethal Weapons Perception Study." Vol. 1 No. 7, Aug. 1998. EPI3087

create the government's authority to exist through consent which, it seems, is best given in advance.

The issue of transparency in government has been a theme I often heard in Europe. It was the idea that government should be as transparent as possible in order to maintain its integrity. It is in the closed caucuses and secret meetings hidden from public view where corruption and unethical behavior is seeded and released on the planet. The need for secrecy has gone beyond what is reasonable. Hiding records for decades after the events when perhaps a few months or years might really be all that is necessary. A review of national security and secrecy laws and their effectiveness is needed. Instead we are seeing an increased level of fear being injected into public opinion leading to even more limits to open disclosure.

When we wrote *Earth Rising – The Revolution* it was intended as a warning of where these technologies were headed. We had hoped that the ideas presented there would have encouraged debate before we had an event like the disaster in the New York World Trade Center attack. That single event took the 650 sources we quoted in that January, 2000 book and made them live in all of their implications. We had put forward the proposition that terrorism would lead to rapid advances in military technologies and an acceleration toward war, which is exactly what we are seeing. We predicted the abandonment of the ABM Treaty (Anti-Ballistic Missile), increases in surveillance systems uses, continued degradation of privacy and the rapid advancements in "non lethal technologies". All of these predictions were borne out over the last three years and continue to unfold even as we write these words.

Electromagnetic Fields?

Many studies have been, and continue to be, conducted in the area of electromagnetic field exposures. Vibratory energy is the essence of all of the issues addressed in this book whether electromagnetic, acoustic or mechanical. Vibration at very specific rates, when delivered in many different forms, can and does result in destruction whether people, computers or other materials. This knowledge has profound implications. The revolution in technologies offers the greatest potentials for humans but must be understood and used in the right way.

"Electromagnetic fields, in differing modalities are known to affect electrically sensitive sites of the human body. High strength fields have the theoretical potential to *incapacitate personnel* by entrainment of brain neuron firing, less strong fields have been known for over a century to cause a visual impairment. At question is whether or not the technology requirements to effect these types of biological incapacitations will be prohibitive for reasons of size, energy, collateral damage or concurrent permanent injury to the targeted human. Answers to these questions will only be forthcoming as more is learned about the actual susceptibility of animals to potential modalities of high-strength electromagnetic fields.

It is well known that animals absorb radio-frequency energy, resulting in heating. *The active biophysical mechanism in the proposed work is* ***not heating*** *but rather lowering the firing potential of neurons, triggering them to discharge, or inducing currents.* The proposed concept offers the potential for graded force, or tunability for a weapon system that could be used at close range or 100+ meters. Several potential levels of effect are possible, ranging from the disruption of visual acuity via induction of magnetophosphenes to disruption of short-term memory (e.g., what happened during the past 5-10 seconds) to total loss of control of voluntary bodily functions (Easterly et al. 1995). Work in this initial proposal will be limited to the latter objective.

Staff of the Oak Ridge National Laboratory (ORNL) propose to undertake a proof-of-principle measurement program designed to determine the potential for electromagnetic fields to be useful as an incapacitating agent in non-lethal technologies. All work during Phases I and II on disruption of voluntary motion will be done with small animals, mice or rats, and will be limited to a proof-of-principle experiment.

If this proof-of-principle experiment is successful, follow-on work not included in this proposal will provide more detailed characterization of the parameters of effects, target size scaling parameters, and methods by which these electromagnetic fields may be directed to distant targets." 232

The above study announcement was designed to further refine knowledge in this area. The Air Force had studied these effects in the 1980s, the Navy in the 1960s and other research teams from various federal departments since the 1960s. We trace this pattern in our earlier work and find it interesting to see the continued move in these new directions of war. These new systems will be used in urban conflicts and where civilians are mixed in with combatants as was the case in Moscow when poison gas was used. A substance is poisonous when lethal doses are applied. This is a clear illustration of the fact that even those things thought to be safe can have a much different effect.

At the same time as the new systems are developed to inflict the force of these weapons, detection technologies also need to be evolved. Remember we are dealing with energy as a weapons base shaping an array of new systems. We must therefore develop those kinds of tools needed for "seeing" the new threats which might also be turned against us. A recent contact called for the following:

"OBJECTIVE: To develop a small, inexpensive portable alarm that will indicate overexposure to electromagnetic fields (3 KHz to 100 GHz).

DESCRIPTION: A personal alarm that has the ability to detect high levels of electromagnetic field exposure (near and far field) is essential for personnel to do their jobs without health hazards in the environments mandated by DoD global operations. Development of a small, inexpensive portable alarm to detect exposure to high intensity electromagnetic fields needs to be completed and brought to market. Currently available detectors/alarms generally cost several hundreds of dollars, making them impractical for mass distribution to military personnel who would wear this product on their clothing or equipment. The alarm should detect magnetic and electrical fields and each field will have separate audible and/or visible indicators. It

232 US Department of Energy, Special Technologies Program. FY99 Project Proposal. Requirement Number: STP-001-99. Project Title: Disruption of Voluntary Motion. Performing Laboratory: Oak Ridge National Laboratory. EPI1271

is predicted that multiple alarms would be worn (e.g., front, back or on helmet) to detect millimeter wave frequencies." 233

The detection technology is for locating the energy emissions they realize are the ones that present the real risks to military personnel. These are the same energy emanations that our new weapons use in causing their effects. The changes are being introduced to mainstream populations with tasers or shocking instruments that make physical contact with the body. However, these newer systems use energy sent wirelessly yet have perhaps more devastating effects than a bullet.

Advanced Gizmos?

"The Defense Department said on Tuesday it was pouring research dollars into high-energy lasers, microwave systems and a host of other advanced gizmos designed to win 21st-century wars more quickly and decisively than ever. Development of such things as unmanned systems for land, air, space, sea and underwater was to counter the spread of 'asymmetric' threats to US forces in the past decade, Pentagon officials told Congress."234 Generalized statements are not sufficient in these matters. An understanding of the effects and risks should be a part of the disclosure.

In early 2001 the Pentagon announced additional initiatives and targets for these new gizmos without many specifics building on the perceived threats which would lead to the North Koreans withdrawing from agreements on their nuclear programs. "The Department of Defense has granted the US Central Command permission to conduct experimental surveillance and 'exclusion' technologies this year in harbors. The Advanced Concept Technology Demonstrations (ACTD) program consists of 14 new projects that will be financed this year by the Pentagon. The ACTD program is intended to enable the military to join together current technologies to meet important needs without having to take part in the long and costly typical acquisition process. The ACTDs approved this year include the implementation of a laser as both a lethal and non-lethal helicopter

---

233 United States Air Force. Air Force Solicitation AF01-066. Title: Electromagnetic Field Overexposure Indicator. EPI3118

234 *Reuters.* "Pentagon trains tech for war." June 26, 2001. *www.zdnet.com* EPI3431

weapon; an inexpensive drone that will sport an electronic jammer; and a combination Army-Navy long-range missile and launcher that can hit hard and deeply concealed North Korean targets. In addition, the ACTD program will include a new computer network intrusion detection system experiment that fights hackers by blocking them from penetrating a network and also by striking back." 235

From DoD to Law Enforcement Applications & Imagination

In the course of this work, as in the first book in this series, we have taken liberally from the public record and tried to quote the material directly in trying to knit this story together. We have said in our presentations around the world "not our words, just their words" when reporting on these matters. We believe that it is our responsibility to help raise the questions we are identifying in these pages. The following brings the issues forward:

> "As effective as they are in their tasks, chemical agents are not nearly perfect due to their limited range, environmental impact, and unpredictable levels of reliability. On the rise are new technologies. One such new agent is the type that affects the olfactory senses of the criminal, especially the male odorants, which effectively make the target his or her own dispersal agent. Capture nets are another emerging technology. Although appealing in theory, the nets are difficult to deploy and use to subdue criminals in all but the most ideal conditions. They are not very effective indoors due to obstructions like furniture, walls, and ceilings. Searching and hand-cuffing a suspect is hindered by the presence of the net, and so far, the nets can only be deployed through projection. The vision for non-lethal law enforcement tools in the future includes the use of light and sound to apprehend criminals. Subjecting suspects to certain kinds of light or directed sound blasts is on the horizon. The technologies that exist presently, and the types envisioned

235 Hess, Pamela. *(UPI).* "Pentagon OKs Experimental Tech Projects." Feb. 2, 2001. *Law Enforcement & Corrections Technology News Summary,* Feb. 8, 2001. EPI3065

for the near future, are considered 'stop-gaps' because they do the necessary job for now, until more effective and humane methods and tools are developed and able to be implemented. Even though current non-lethal technologies are not perfect, when used properly they ensure a degree of respect for the dignity and safety accorded any human life." 236

"Non-lethal weapons currently in development include what chemists at the University of New Hampshire have described as microcapsules. Microcapsules dissolve and activate in response to heat, pressure, ultraviolet light, human sweat, or salt water. M-2 Technologies is hoping that microcapsules will someday be used to stop vessels by expanding inside their cooling systems. According to Janet Morris, microcapsules can also be used to clear an area by releasing the intense smell of feces or rotting corpses – so intense, in fact, that it will cause people to retch or vomit. The Marine Corps is experimenting with a non-lethal foam used to disarm small-caliber weapons or, in its adhesive form, to disable people. Other non-lethal tactics currently in development include the use of disorienting sound waves, and the employment of spider silk in bulletproof vests and helmets. The silk, twice as tough as Kevlar, could possibly be developed into a lightweight bulletproof fabric." 237

A system was even developed to cause chemicals to be put in an area on on the skin which would only be activated by the right kind of energy being directed at them. "A system for enhancing and improving the transcutaneous or transdermal delivery of topical chemicals or drugs. A disposable container contains a substantially sterile unit dose of an active agent adapted for a single use in a medical treatment. The unit dose is formulated to enhance transport of the active agent

236 Heal, Sid. *(Law Enforcement Technology)*. "The Push for Less-Lethal." Nov. 2000, Vol. 27, No. 11. *Law Enforcement & Corrections Technology News Summary*, Dec. 14, 2000. EPI2919

237 Barry, Ellen. *(Boston Globe)*. "Non-Lethal Weapons: Sci-Fi Meets Pentagon Mass. Couples' Far-Out Ideas Gaining Military's Respect." Nov. 20, 2000. *Law Enforcement & Corrections Technology News Summary*, Nov. 22, 2000. EPI2920

through mammalian skin when the active agent is applied to the skin and the skin is exposed to light and/or ultrasound defined by at least one specific parameter." 238

The Joint Non-Lethal Weapons Program

These are programs as of April 2000, almost three years ago at the time of this writing. Most of these ideas have provided the framework for the completion of many advanced technologies, which will be used in coming conflicts with increased visibility to the public as fear increases and insecurity is elevated by the media propaganda surrounding every event.

In wartime we have to remember the words of those who will use these technologies. "It is not the primary purpose of nonlethal weapons to prevent death or major injury to opposing troops. Instead, they are intended to increase the lethality of force used against combatants, while reducing death and injury among noncombatant civilians. For example, NLW can prevent a crowd from approaching closely enough to be a serious threat to US forces. They can also unmask snipers or other combatants in a crowd of civilians, opening a field for US lethal fire. In short, NLW are important because they permit military engagement at a lower level of violence. And in political terms, less violence equals more acceptability." 239

These technologies have been in use for over a decade and evolving throughout the period. The restrains come only after the fact as was the case with blinding lasers. "First of course, it is technically possible to use these kinds of weapons against people, so some people have put them in the 'nonlethal technology' category. There is a policy, however, against using them to blind individuals. Still, such devices can be used effectively for non-blinding applications. For instance, we supported the Marines in

238 US Patent #6,030,374. February 29, 2000. Title: "Ultrasound enhancement of percutaneous drug absorption." Inventor: McDaniel, David H. EPI3251

239 Council On Foreign Relations. "Nonlethal Technologies: Progress and Prospects."
http://www.foreignrelations.org/public/pubs/NonViolentTaskforce.html
EPI1294

Somalia with low-level laser devices that can illuminate and designate targets, including human beings."240 These are systems which clearly violate a rational war when one considers those who wield these weapons are also subject to them. Will these introductions start the next arms race, one which offers our adversaries immense power? We do not think so. We know that many of these kinds of energy discharges can be monitored with absolute precision globally. Energy emissions are as unique as the finger prints of a person. Guarding misuse means disclosure and discussion of any instances where these technologies can be used. The implications to our health, environment and future generations depends upon the wisdom of man's uses of technology. We possess or will very shortly possess numerous new methods for destroying life, humanity and the soul. What choices will we make?

Tests Hidden Away Behind the Iron Curtain

"One day, back in the 1970s, a sudden mass disease swept the barracks near Riga Lijia 6849 0502 and Gomel Gemaier 2047 7796 1422 in the western part of the former Soviet Union. The rank and file became unconscious; some even went insane. Where did this sudden 'army disease' come from? No one knew at that time. Many doctors were mystified. Later, it was learned that some military technology scientists were testing infrasonic waves nearby, and this 'army disease' was caused by their fallout." 241 These systems are very powerful and more disruptive than any could imagine outside of science fiction. These technologies date back decades and are clearly those which present the greatest challenges. At the same time a great deal can be learned and the knowledge applied toward healing rather than killing. This is where the answer is – where we might repair the damage to the Earth rather than continue to destroy it. The idea that the stewards of the planet, those of us existing here together, cannot turn these technologies to solving conflict rather than amplifying it, is the nature of humankind in a fallen state. In our

240 *IEEE Spectrum.* Interview with US Air Force Major General Richard R. Paul. March 1996. EPI1274

241 Chuandao, Han. "New Concept Weaponry." *Beijing Guofang National Defense.* No. 4, April 15, 1997. Central Intelligence Agency, Aug. 1997. Approved for release Jan. 2001. Obtained by Freedom of Information Act request by Harlan Girard. EPI3269

lifetimes we may never see the change. Perhaps peace will only come when we realize that death by any name is still death and war is still war and humans can change it all...

Propaganda Wars Heat Up

"A Defense Department advisory panel's recommendation that the US Special Operations Command (SOCOM) phase out its Commando Solo psychological warfare aircraft and replace it with a range of newer platforms has sparked a debate about the command's modernization priorities. It has also helped shed light on the role that these units play in US military operations." 242 These systems are not limited to dropping leaflets or radio broadcasts. These systems include putting signals on broadcasts in an area for psychoactive effects, which can be achieved, as was pointed out, through several sources in the public record. These systems can directly interact with the brain and body in a manner which can either kill or incapacitate depending on the intention of the operator and vulnerability of the victim.

"In the area of psychological warfare, author Liu Ping stressed that China recognizes special information media, such as language, texts, images and sound, as future enemy weapons capable of exerting a 'multilevel operational effect' instead of simply a political or economic one. The target remains the enemy's decision making processes, both human (the mind's soft data processor) and material (hardware data processing). The main task is to overwhelm opposing forces through the use of terror tactics, thereby upsetting their psychological stability. Psychological war usually starts in peacetime and, if war erupts, will run throughout its course." 243

"The National Institute of Justice (NIJ) has agreed that both an extension of the current MOA between DoD and DoJ, and a new memorandum of understanding between NIJ and the Joint Program, are important to continued cooperation in the area of non-lethal technologies. The concept of dual-use technologies, which assumes that there are some systems and munitions that

242 Kennedy, Harold. *(National Defense)*. "Psyops Units Encouraged to Modernize Their Equipment." http://nationaldefense.ndia.org EPI3326

243 Thomas, Timothy L. (Foreign Military Studies Office). "Human Network Attacks." *Military Review*, September-October 1999. EPI3233

have utility to both law enforcement and the military, drives both organizations closer to cooperative efforts." 244

High Power Microwave Weapons

"The fast international development towards increasingly complicated and miniaturized microwave circuits (MMIC) is creating new opportunities in defense applications like radar, electronic warfare and communication. Active antenna arrays will be the foundation for many future defense applications." 245 These technologies are not limited to these systems alone. Those with a direct impact on people were the subject of widespread press reports in 1999 and 2000 when the Marines announced a new weapon system. What they did not mention is the tunability of millimeter waves in causing a variety of effects not just the sensation of burning on the skin. The fact is that these new systems can heat the body, stop the heart or impact any other organ of the body from the brain to the bowels and cause involuntary reactions and death. The energy from these devices can be pulsed, shaped, or altered in frequency and form in such a way as to provide a wide array of effects as an active system of energy dispersal.

"Active Denial Technology is a breakthrough non-lethal technology that uses millimeter-wave electromagnetic energy to stop, deter and turn back an advancing adversary from relatively long range. It is expected to save countless lives by providing a way to stop individuals without causing injury, before a deadly confrontation develops. Active Denial Technology uses a transmitter to send a narrow beam of energy towards an identified subject. Traveling at the speed of light, the energy reaches the subject and penetrates less than 1/64 of an inch into the skin, quickly heating up the skin's surface. Within seconds an individual feels an intense heating sensation that stops when the transmitter is shut off or when the individual moves out of the

244 *Joint NLW Directorate News*. "NIJ-JNLWP Join Efforts." Vol. 1 No. 7, Aug. 1998. EPI3086

245 Swedish Defence Research Agency (FOI). "Department of Microwave Technology." www.foa.se/english/institutions/980764991.html EPI3291

beam." 246 Speed of light transmission of energy...186,000 mile per second...Changing warfare forever. Energy is the essence of these new weapons and civilian threats.

Biggest Breakthrough Since the Atomic Bomb

"The Marine Corps is preparing to unveil perhaps the biggest breakthrough in weapons since the atomic bomb – a nonlethal weapon that fires directed energy at human targets....*Marine Corps Times* reports that the weapon, called the V-Mounted Active Denial System is designed to stop an individual in his tracks and make him turn and flee.

Plans now call for an unveiling and demonstration for military and congressional leaders in March at Kirtland Air Force Base, N.M." 247"Though detailed information about the weapon's design remain classified, the story stated that the weapon would heat a target's skin to approximately 130 degrees Fahrenheit in about two seconds. Humans start to feel pain at 113 degrees. The *[Marine Corps Times]* report went on to say that soldiers could fire the weapon from distances exceeding 750 meters (2,250 feet) from their target – a range that would allow them to remain outside the reach of most small arms fire." 248

Other reports mentioned the lethal aspects of this new tool in the military arsenal. "The US Marine Corps is set to unveil a weapon that directs a field of energy in the microwave range of the electromagnetic spectrum. The Vehicle-Mounted Active Denial System is considered perhaps the biggest breakthrough in weapons technology since the atomic bomb. The amount of time the device must be trained on a person to cause death and its effective range are still classified information." 249 "The weapon is designed to stop people by firing millimeter-wave electro-

---

246 Air Force Research Laboratory, Office of Public Affairs. "Active Denial Technology." Fact Sheet. EPI3278

247 *Army Times Publishing Company*. "*Marine Corps Times* reports on secret weapon program." Feb. 23, 2001. EPI3077

248 Hearn, Kelly. *(UPI)*. "New non-lethal energy weapon heats skin." Feb. 26, 2001. EPI3097

249 Leavitt, Paul. *(USA Today)*. "Marines Working on Microwave Weapon." Feb. 27, 2001. *Law Enforcement & Corrections Technology News Summary*, March 1, 2001. EPI3113

magnetic energy in a beam that quickly heats up the surface of the victim's skin. Within seconds the person feels pain that officials said is similar to touching a hot light bulb. The device, called the Vehicle Mounted Active Denial System, has been tested on 72 people at Brooks Air Force Base, Texas, since 1994." 250

Even while acknowledging death could occur in some reports the same team would deny these effects as serious in others. Questions began to be raised..."Tests of a controversial weapon that is designed to heat people's skin with a microwave beam have shown that it can disperse crowds. But critics are not convinced the system is safe. Last week, the Air Force Research Laboratory (AFRL) in New Mexico finished testing the system on human volunteers. The Air Force now wants to use this Active Denial Technology (ADT), which it says is non-lethal, for peacekeeping or riot control at 'relatively long range' – possibly from low-flying aircraft."251 The effects were downplayed by the public relations experts of the military. Our old foe Rich Garcia was back on the scene. Rich was the person that came in to rescue the Program Manager of HAARP when he continued to create problems by getting caught talking too much and playing games with the facts. Rich Garcia commented on the project in the soft sell of non-lethal lingo. "A nonlethal weapon designed to incapacitate people by firing pain-causing micro-millimeter waves will be tested at Kirtland Air Force Base, N.M. 'It's the kind of pain you would feel if you were being burned,' said Rich Garcia, a spokesman for the Air Force Research Laboratory at the base. 'It's just not intense enough to cause any damage.' The device works by firing micro-millimeter waves that penetrate just beneath a person's skin, heating it by a few dozen degrees and causing severe pain." 252

"The Pentagon today unveiled what some military officials hope will become the rubber bullet of the 21st century: a weapon that uses electromagnetic waves to disperse crowds without killing, maiming or, military officials say, even injuring

250 *AP*. "Pentagon unveils non-lethal weapon." March 2, 2001. *www.marinetimes.com* EPI3108

251 Hecht, Jeff. *(New Scientist)*. "Microwave beam weapon to disperse crowds." Oct. 1, 2001. *www.newscientist.com* EPI3711

252 *AP*. "Kirtland to test non-lethal weapon." March 1, 2001. *www.marinetimes.com* EPI3096

anyone slightly. As envisioned by its Pentagon planners, the weapon would fire bursts of electromagnetic energy capable of causing burning sensations on the skin of people standing as far as 700 yards away – without actually burning them, officials said." 253 The military public relations effort began to leak when researchers, respected around the world and under contract to military planners for years, began to speak out on these issues. Dr. Ross Adey was one such outspoken individual.

"Claims by US military officials that a new skin-heating weapon causes no permanent health problems are exaggerated and highly suspect, experts told *United Press International* on Tuesday. Possible long-term side-effects could include cancer and cataracts, they said. Their claims are a bunch of crap,' said Professor W. Ross Adey, professor of physiology at Loma Linda University Medical Center in Loma Linda, Calif. 'We've known that many forms of microwaves at levels below heating can cause significant health effects in the long term.'" 254 Press reports began to mount and concerns reached many around the world but disappeared from public view in the United States without any political action or serious inquiry by the Congress. "The 'People Zapper' [VMADS] is turning into a political hot potato. The whole world is interested in the Corps' futuristic directed-energy weapon – maybe more interested, in fact, than the Corps itself. But while critics wait to throw water on the concept and police agencies and others wait anxiously for its development, Marines already are developing tactics for the new weapon."255

"The future of the 'People Zapper' is in the hands of a few colonels and generals. The Joint Non-Lethal Weapons Directorate wants to move ahead with the weapon, a revolutionary directed-energy weapon designed for use against humans. But the services are not so sure." 256

253 Dao, James. "Pentagon Unveils Plans for a New Crowd-Dispersal Weapon." March 2, 2001. *www.nytimes.com* EPI3165

254 Hearn, Kelly. *(UPI)*. "Scientists dispute military 'raygun' claims." March 6, 2001. EPI3144

255 Brinkley, C. Mark. "Zapper Tactics." July 30, 2001. *Marine Corps Times.* EPI3501

256 Brinkley, C. Mark. "Senior officials have unique task in assessing weapon's future." July 30, 2001. *Marine Corps Times.* EPI3502

"Some testing on potential uses of the weapon [VMADS] is already underway by the Center for Emerging Threats and Opportunities (CETO), a partnership between the Marine Corps Warfighting Lab and the Potomac Institute for Policy Studies, an Arlington, VA.-based think tank." 257 "'The [VMADS] technology fires millimeter waves on a frequency of 95 gigahertz, which falls between microwaves and infrared light on the electromagnetic spectrum', [Dr. Kirk] Hackett said. The waves differ from microwave energy used to cook food, Hackett said, primarily because those waves travel at 2.5 gigahertz and sink much deeper into the object, cooking food from the inside out for several minutes." 258 Tunability is again the key as the above reports indicate. Other reports began to describe the possibility of impacting even land mines.

"For years it has been suggested that high power microwaves (HPM) would be an appropriate tool for clearance of land mines. However, proof of the effectiveness of such a clearance method is largely missing. This study – which mainly consists of a screening test using a powerful outdoor test facility – was carried out in order to investigate how various components in land mines respond to high intensity microwave radiation. Our conclusion is that HPM is not presently effective for mine clearance, but that HPM might be used to destroy mine detectors and various electronic units for control of mine fields." 259 Later reports have indicated that new systems for mine sweeping are being created using energy from HPM.

Targeting Hardware

"The High Power Microwave Division of the Air Force Research laboratory's Directed Energy Directorate develops technology to generate High Power Microwave radiation, propagate it to a target, assess target effects and system response, and demonstrate effectiveness and utility of compact HPM

257 Brinkley, Mark. "Groups Consider Field Applications For Human Zapper." July 30-Aug. 5. *Defense News* EPI3606

258 Brinkley, C. Mark. "US Marines Test Nonlethal Riot-Suppression Device." *Defense News*, March 12, 2001. EPI3182

259 Listh et al. "Using microwave radiation to neutralise land mines." FOA Report – Abstract. Stockholm, FOA 2000. EPI3293

systems integrated into various Air Force platforms. This technology is useful for a variety of weapon and radar missions.

High Power Microwave technology builds on a firm foundation provided by the Electromagnetic Pulse Technology. Unlike electromagnetic pulse, however, it has higher frequency content and is much more penetrating into target systems. High Power Microwave produces burnout and disruption in electronics while not affecting humans. It has low collateral damage potential and may be useful in a variety of non-lethal missions, where more conventional weapons may not be employed because of fears of civilian casualties or physical damage to nearby sites.

In-house Division capabilities include modeling and simulation of High Power microwave sources, effects and engagements; pulse-power development; HPM source and antenna development; field demonstrations, and system studies.

Research and development on both narrowband and wide-band High Power Microwave sources has been successful in producing devices that are among the world's most powerful microwave pulse emitters. The impulse Radiating Antenna technology, developed within the Division, has been demonstrated as focusing ultra-wide-band radiation into a conical beam with a beam width of approximately a single degree. The hydrogen switch technology has recently been demonstrated effective in an Advanced Concept Technology Demonstration.

The solid state switch technology offers the same type of ultra-wide-band beam, but with the ability to make the antenna conformal to the skin of a system. With the promise of high efficiency, the technology also provides the ability to steer the beam phase the radiation [sic] into an extremely narrow beam. In the narrow-beam HPM area there are several technologies under development including the Magnetic Insulated Line Oscillator technology which offers the promise of compatibility with explosive pulse generators for converting a tremendous amount of energy into microwaves. The High Power Microwave Division facilities are the best in the world, with all the necessary functions located at Kirtland Air Force Base, New Mexico." 260

260 Air Force Research Laboratory, Office of Public Affairs. "High Power Microwaves." Fact Sheet, Jan. 1998. EPI3282

"Patent applications for detectors of HPM-radiation have been submitted and one of them is now patent pending as Swedish Patent 507 085. With the patent pending invention, it is possible to distinguish field strength, wavelength and polarization of the HPM-radiation. Photographic films and thermal printing paper have successfully been used as a detector indicator in tests at FOA in Sweden with a HPM generator operating at 37 GHz.

The patent pending HPM-detector is available in both passive and active versions. The advantage of the passive detector is that it would be cheap to fabricate and could therefore be extensively deployed. The possibilities to generate short microwave pulses of extremely high pulse power by means of more and more compact devices imply a new electromagnetic threat for both the National Defense and the civil society. Equipment for generation of high-energy microwave pulses can be mounted on different types of vehicles, and can thereby easily be moved for achievements of hidden sabotage against establishments of different kinds, for instance against stores containing defense electronic and systems forming part of the telecommunication network. An aggressor could use such mobile microwave weapons for carrying out sabotage activities, for instance in order to eliminate the function of stored electronic systems, even when they are not activated.

A forewarning that HPM irradiation has occurred could deprive the aggressor the time advantage and chaos he hopes to gain from this kind of hidden sabotage activities. Therefore there is a military need of a sensor which can detect that an object has been exposed to potentially harmful microwave pulses.

Such a sensor could also have civil applications. It could for instance be ascertained whether exposure to powerful microwave pulses might have caused the accident or incident. Computer installations could also be provided with such sensors in order to render possible a check whether system errors could be due to microwave exposure. Another civil application of the HPM detector for short pulse detection intended for biological health monitoring of microwaves. When biological safety standards for microwave short pulse exposure for personnel are agreed and established, there will be a need for a product to monitor HPM-pulses of short duration and the invented HPM-detectors would fill this need." 261

Infrasound & Ultrasonics

These are the most frightening weapons of the 21st century as the ideas continue to advance. We have reported on these technologies with increasing levels of concern with the passage of the last eight years. It is these technologies which now present the greatest challenge to human values on the level of the soul. Will we allow these intrusions into the essence of who we are as human beings?

"Acoustic Weapons: The emission of energy at a certain frequency makes it possible to destroy enemy personnel and radioelectronic facilities. Military generators can be installed on delivery systems at sea, in the air, and in space. They have potential for use on balloons.

By directing an energy emission at a target or creating background energy emissions it is possible to turn an enemy division into a herd of frightened idiots. People will experience inexplicable fear and a severe headache and their actions will become unpredictable. They may become totally and irreversibly deranged." 262

"Neither fortifications nor armor will save one against the effect of acoustic or psychotronic weapons. Attaining the very same goals with traditional weapons requires a very large expenditure of various ammunition. In addition, nonlethal weapons increase the effect radius of precision weapons as it were, and their swiftness, concealment of deployment and surprise of use reinforce their psychological effect." 263

261 EME Electro Magnetic Engineering. "High Power Microwave (HPM) detectors invented at FOA." www.eme.se/EME_News.html EPI3289

262 Khokhlov, Aleksandr. "Army Must 'Develop Science' To Keep Up." (Report on a conversation with military analyst Major General Vladimir Slipchenko). *Moscow Komsomolskaya Pravda,* Oct. 15, 1996. Central Intelligence Agency, Oct. 1996. Approved for release Jan. 2001. Obtained by Freedom of Information Act request by Harlan Girard. EPI3270

263 Borisov et al. "Future War: Growing Role of Non-Lethal Weapons." *Moscow Nezavisimoye Voyennoye Obozreniya.* May 22-28, 1998. No. 19. Central Intelligence Agency, July 1998. Approved for release May 2001. Obtained by Harlan Girard through Freedom of Information Act request. EPI3530

"An Acoustic Blaster demonstration program is currently underway at PRIMEX Physics International. A prototype blaster, consisting of an array of four(4) combustion detonation-driven devices has been developed and tested successfully. The prototype containing the four acoustic devices are capable of being fired simultaneously or independently. The most encouraging result thus far, is that acoustic pressure up to 165 dB at 50 ft. from the source has already been achieved. Equally important is that output pressure waveform of the prototype blaster...appears to contain very desirable risetime and pulsewidth characteristics that are essential for optimal acoustic-physiological coupling to targets for anti-personnel applications." 264 Remember the formulas for sound in air verses sound in water. At this level in air serious damage can occur.

"A variety of acoustic sources are being developed and tested for possible application as special weapons for use in scenarios such as crowd control and area denial that call for less-than-lethal force application. These sources include devices that generate acoustic energy by repetitive combustion or detonation of a fuel-oxidizer mixture. These devices are attractive for development as fieldable weapons because they offer the advantages of simplicity of design and very high-intensity acoustic output from relatively small packages powered by common chemical fuels. The acoustic signals produced by these devices are typically repetitive impulsive waveforms similar to those generated by explosives..." 265 The difference is that they are coherent signals created for a specific biological or hardware effect depending on the tunable parameters of the technology being used. These new energy weapons are the key to the 21st century war fighting machine and also are their most vulnerable. Defensive systems, detection technologies and deployment technologies have been the subject of billions of dollars, on a global scale, without significant debate. The debate is rising however as has been demonstrated over the years by all of those taking on these and other related issues.

264 Sze et al. (Primex Physics International Company). "Non-Lethal Weapons: An Acoustic Blaster Demonstration Program." Non-Lethal Defense III, Feb. 1998. EPI3173

265 Boesch et al. (Army Research Laboratory). "A High-Power Electrically Driven Acoustic Source for Target Effects Experiments and Area-Denial Applications." Non-Lethal Defense III, Feb. 1998. EPI3176

How do they Work

"Prior research indicates that an array of ultrasonic sources operated with an offset in frequency will produce infrasonic or very low frequency energy. This energy is useful because it is omni-directional, and it propagates well with little absorption. With sufficient energy, the resulting infrasonic waves can be disabling or lethal. Synetics proposes an approach toward developing infrasonic waves that can ultimately be incorporated into future man-portable small arms weapon systems. This approach utilizes modernized pneumatic technology which produces an extremely high-powered ultrasonic source. The resulting frequency generated is precisely controlled such that the desired high power infrasound frequency can be generated at the target by beating two focused ultrasonic sources.

The subsonic weapons now being researched can be basically divided into two types. The first is the 'nerve-type' subsonic weapons, with vibration frequencies very close to that of the alpha rhythm (8-12 hertz) of the human brain, resulting in neural confusion. When producing resonance, it can powerfully stimulate the human brain, resulting in neural confusion." 266 What is being said here is that outside oscillations or pulses of energy in many forms can cause big changes in what happens in the human brain. As a result of the use of these new technologies any regulatory system of the body can be disrupted as the brain is the master control. Overriding our natural energetic systems, is the new essence of the technology – torture or non-lethal – we, the authors, ask?

"Some major military countries started research on infrasound weapons during 60s to 70s. Infrasound was proven capable of damaging human sensory and internal organs and disabling people. A small amount of output power can cause unstable mental state and body malfunction, or even symptoms of mental disease. An advanced infrasound generator targeting personnel has been designed and tested, with the amount of energy of the generated infrasound wave adjustable to cause

266 *Beijing Jiefangjun Bao*. "High-Energy Microwave Weapons." Dec. 25, 1995. Central Intelligence Agency. Approved for public release May 2001. Obtained by Harlan Girard through Freedom of Information Act request. EPI3528

personnel disorientation, nausea, vomiting and incontinence." 267 These systems are much more advanced today, and are continuing to advance as science and technology moves forward.

Lethal Energy Weapons

"A daily dose of radio waves may help destroy invasive zebra mussels, the tiny freshwater snails that are clogging up the waterways of North America. Beaming extremely low frequency electromagnetic (ELF-EM) radiation at the mussels causes their body chemistry to go awry, killing them within a matter of weeks, the new research shows. The effect seems specific for zebra mussels, says [Purdue University chemist Matthew] Ryan." 268 This use of energy was specific to this creature. This is the basis for the development of an array of technologies that can kill based on genetic specific vulnerability or agitation or on the basis of specific resonance effects triggered by coherent energy sources.

The former head of the Soviet Union was also aware of these systems and commented on them in 1989 long before US announcements. The evidence is clear of the research roots decades before."Boris Yeltsin...has told a reporter that the KGB has an ELF device that can stop a human heart from beating...Yeltsin said that KGB agents told him that they have a device which emits a powerful 7-11 Hz signal which can stop the heart. According to Yeltsin, the KGB agents said that, "If emergency medical aid isn't close at hand, it's all over." 269

RMA Revisited

There was a paper we commented on extensively in both *Angels Don't Play This HAARP* and in *Earth Rising – The Revolution* which was called the *Revolution and Military Affairs*

267 *Beijing Renmin Junyi.* "New Weapons, Medical-Related Problems." Vol. 40, No. 9, Sept. 1997. Description of source: *Beijing Renmin Junyi* in Chinese – monthly journal of the People's Liberation Army General Logistics Department, Health Department, carrying many technical articles on military medicine, on rare occasions contains articles on chemical and biological warfare. Central Intelligence Agency. Obtained by Freedom of Information Act requested by Harlan Girard, 2001. EPI3381

268 Zandonella, Catherine. "Radio waves destroy pest zebra mussels." Aug. 1, 2001. *www.newscientist.com* EPI3854

269 *Microwave News.* "The KGB Signal." November/December 1989. EPI1279

and Conflicts Short of War produced by the US Army War College in 1990. This document suggested that the new technologies of the 21st century would be used as fear of drugs and terrorists grew. The paper suggested that by amplifying fear Americans would drop their traditional values in exchange for safety and security. Have you seen the advertisements – Terrorists & Drugs the theme? This was put forward as the way these new technologies would be allowed to be used by the United States over the objections of civil society. In the direction we are headed, motivated by fear, we will make grave errors that will change the way we see war. In that the paper it talked about shooting down suspected drug traffickers and the complications when trials, juries and judges are forgotten? What about errors? Are we the hooded executioners hidden behind the technology forgetting the Constitution we are charged to protect? In many instances the reality played out... "The Peruvian government, with US surveillance assistance, has shot down or strafed more than 100 airplanes since 1992 as part of a program aimed at reducing the flood of cocaine into the United States, US intelligence officials said yesterday. The United States began limited air surveillance and interdiction in Peru and other South American countries in 1992 under the Bush administration. It continued and escalated through 1998, when the Clinton administration shut the program down because of 'other pressing needs.'"270 Juries, judges, due process – what happened to these? These are the issues first raised in 1990 in the RMA paper just quoted.

And mistakes did happen. "Relatives of US missionaries whose plane was shot down over the Amazon River said the aircraft received clearance to land moments before the Peruvian air force fired on it without warning. A US intelligence official said Sunday that the crew of a CIA-operated surveillance plane in the area had notified the Peruvian military that the plane might be trafficking drugs but later 'voiced objections' to downing the craft."271 There is always a desire to use the technology when missions are confused. Is it right to use the military in civilian matters where death may not be the desired outcome?

---

270 Seper, Jerry. "Peru downs planes with help of US in drug program." April 24, 2001. *www.washtimes.com* EPI3234

271 *CBS* with *AP* and *Reuters*. "Shoot-Down Scenario Disputed." April 23, 2001. *www.cbsnews.com* EPI3228

Farwell Brain Fingerprinting

"Farwell Brain Fingerprinting is a revolutionary new technology for investigating crimes and exonerating innocent suspects, with a record of 100% accuracy in research on FBI agents, research with US government agencies, and field applications. Brain fingerprinting solves the central problem by determining scientifically whether a suspect has the details of a crime stored in his brain." 272 "The brainchild of Lawrence Farwell, Brain Fingerprinting is a computer-based technology to identify the perpetrator of a crime accurately and scientifically by measuring brain-wave responses to crime-relevant words or picture presented on a computer screen." 273 "According to Dr. Larry Farwell, the inventor of this technology, 'Brain Fingerprinting is based on the principle that the brain is central to all human activities; it plans, executes and records information. Therefore, if a subject has information pertaining to a crime, this information is permanently recorded in the brain. With proper training and technology, the memories stored in the brain can be retrieved." 274

"Brain fingerprinting works as follows. Words or pictures relevant to a crime are flashed on a computer screen, along with other, irrelevant words or pictures. Electrical brain responses are measured non-invasively through a headband equipped with sensors. Scientific research has shown that a specific brain-wave response called a MERMER (memory and encoding related multifaceted electroencephalographic response) is elicited when the brain processes noteworthy information it recognizes. Thus, when details of the crime that only the perpetrator would know are presented, a MERMER is emitted by the brain of a perpetrator, but not by the brain of an innocent suspect. In Brain Fingerprinting, a computer analyzes the brain response to detect MERMER, and thus determines scientifically

272 Human Brain Research Laboratory Inc. "Brain Fingerprinting: A New Paradigm in Criminal Investigations." *www.brainwavescience.com* EPI3037
273 Dalbey, Beth. "Farwell's Brain Fingerprinting traps serial killer in Missouri." *The Fairfield Ledger. www.brainwavescience.com* EPI3038
274 Burke, Tod. "Brain Fingerprinting: Latest Tool for Law Enforcement." *Law and Order,* June 1999. EPI3039

whether or not the specific crime-relevant information is stored in the brain of the suspect." 275

"The admissibility of Brain Fingerprinting in court has not yet been established. The following well established features of Brain Fingerprinting, however, will be relevant when the question of admissibility is tested in court. 1) Brain Fingerprinting has been thoroughly and scientifically tested. 2) The theory and application of Brain Fingerprinting have been subject to peer review and publication. 3) The rate of error is extremely low – virtually nonexistent – and clear standards governing techniques of operation of the technology have been established and published. 4) The theory and practice of Brain Fingerprinting have gained general acceptance in the relevant scientific community. 5) Brain Fingerprinting is noninvasive and non-testimonial." 276 "The FBI says it is cautiously optimistic the truth detector will stand up in court. The highly secretive CIA is also intrigued, and is funding some of the research. Farwell says his truth detector has been 100% accurate so far. It's all based on the simple theory that even if people choose to lie, the brain always tells the truth." 277 "Ten law enforcement agencies at the local, state, and national levels in the Washington, DC area and in Iowa have agreed to implement Farwell Brain Fingerprinting once appropriate funding is obtained. With the application Farwell Brain Fingerprinting, a new and significant scientific breakthrough has become a practical applied technology. A new era in law enforcement and intelligence has begun. Now there is no reason why any individual should ever again be falsely convicted of a crime, nor should any guilty person evade justice for lack of evidence."278 "The potential benefit of this program extends to a broad range of law enforcement applications, including organized

---

275 Farwell, Lawrence. "Forensic Science Report: Brain Fingerprinting Test on Terry Harrington, Re: State of Iowa vs. Terry Harrington." Human Brain Research Laboratory, Inc. May 21, 2000. EPI3041

276 Farwell, Lawrence. "Technical Report on Field applications of Brain Fingerprinting." Human Brain Research Laboratory, Inc. May 12, 2000. EPI3042

277 O'Connell, Jim. Interview with Lawrence Farwell. *Canadian TV Network News. www.brainwavescience.com* EPI3045

278 Farwell, Lawrence. "Farwell Brain Fingerprinting: A New Paradigm in Criminal Investigations." Human Brain Research Laboratory, Inc. Jan. 12, 1999. EPI3043

crime, violent crime, white-collar crime, drug-related crime, foreign counterintelligence, nontraditional targets, and other categories of casework as well. This new technology promises to be of tremendous benefit both at the national level and for state and local law enforcement." 279

Again the implications are enormous and potential for sorting out crime, while increasing transparency of otherwise innocent private persons is at issue. These technologies also lead to the more unusual uses such as creation of synthetic memory for training or other purposes. These technologies are expected, and likely well on their way, according to many reports quoted in our earlier books on these subjects. Issues of interrogation, privacy, and the meaning of the 5th amendment in the advent of these technologies are extraordinarily important in determining how and when these technologies might be used. The idea of integration of these systems into advertising strategies, political issues development or other areas becomes subject to abuse.

The ultimate invasion of privacy is interference with brain functions. "A technology, known as bio-fusion, combines sensors to examine biological systems to understand how information and neural structures produce thought and to display the thought in mathematical terms. By creating an advanced database containing these terms, researchers now can look at brain activity and determine if a person is lying, receiving instructions incorrectly or concentrating on certain thought types that may indicate aggression." 280 Reading people's minds has moved from parlor games to high-tech intrusion into what goes on in one's head. Is this a direction civil society should go?

Health Possibilities

"Surgeons are preparing to create the first husband and wife cyborgs: they intend to implant computer chips in a British professor and his wife to see if they can communicate sensation and movement by thought alone. The professor hopes it will show

---

279 Farwell, Lawrence et al. "Detection of FBI Agents with the Farwell MERA System: A New Paradigm for Psychophysiological Detection of Concealed Information." Human Brain Research Laboratory, Inc. May 7, 1993. EPI3044

280 Berry, Sharon. *(SIGNAL Magazine 2001)*. "Decoding Minds, Foiling Adversaries." Oct. 2001. *www.us.net/signal/Currentissue/Oct01/decoding-oct.html* EPI3710

how two brains can interact; doctors at Stoke Mandeville hospital, who will perform the surgery, hope it will lead to new treatments for paralysis victims." 281

"For decades, doctors have used pacemakers to regulate the heart. Now they're implanting similar devices into the brain. Thousands of patients with the most serious cases of Parkinson's disease and epilepsy have received the devices since they obtained approval in 1997 from the Food and Drug Administration. Hundreds more are slated to take part in clinical trials to see if the pacemakers' electrical impulses can control chronic pain, depression and even obesity." 282

"Researchers elsewhere have previously implanted electrodes in monkeys and people and shown the brain signals can move a cursor. The new work increases the speed and accuracy with which the brain can direct the cursor. Researchers think they are perhaps a decade from perfecting the technique for paralyzed patients." 283

The understanding of the brain and methods of interacting with it without the use of chemicals but, rather, with energy itself is well underway. This direction of research will provide many health answers as we increase our understanding of the human body as an open system subject to the influence of subtle energy changes.We will then rediscover the solution to some of our most oppressive human health conditions.

---

281 Dobson, Roger. "Professor set to 'control' wife by cyborg implant." *Sunday Times,* May 6, 2001. EPI3286

282 Shachtman, Noah. *(Wired News).* "This is your brain on electricity." Aug. 28, 2001. *http://wired.com* EPI3595

283 *Washington Post.* "Brain implant may be missing link between mind, computer." March 13, 2002. *Anchorage Daily News* EPI3920

Chapter 6

Personal Privacy Not a Reasonable Expectation?

Increasingly we have heard rumblings regarding privacy issues in the aftermath of terror and its resulting fear. Identification systems are increasingly coming onto the scene in a manner which will change everything in terms of expectations of what is private. We have traced these systems over the last few years and reported on them in depth in January 2000 through the first book in this series. Our predictions and concerns have moved into the forefront of the public in recent days with a much different feel than those evident in the 1990s.

In the aftermath of September 11, 2001, a significant shift occurred in public opinion. The issues of privacy are being laid aside in exchange for what people are being told will add security to our lives. These technologies will allow for the tracking of all people on the planet if these technologies move forward unchecked. This chapter deals with a few of these technologies which have made the greatest impact in recent days.

ID Systems and Human Tracing

The newest identification systems begin with biometrics. "Biometrics are unique, measurable characteristics of our human make-up. They may be physical or behavioral characteristics. The main biometric technologies include: Face Recognition, Finger Scanning, Finger Geometry, Hand Geometry, Iris Recognition, Palm Prints, Retina, Signature and Voice." 284

"The use of computerized biometrics – systems that read individual body measurements or patterns such as fingerprints, voices, iris prints, or facial features – is gaining widespread use. From banks' experiments with iris scanners to the US Army's

284 Visionics Corporation. "An Overview of Biometric Technology." www.faceit.com EPI2572

massive biometric database, different sectors are dabbling in this technology. Indeed, experts project the commercial biometrics market to increase tenfold in the next three years. The technology dates back more than 100 years to Argentina, where police began documenting fingerprints at the scenes of crimes." 285 In the last three years these issues have moved out of the shadows into the mainstream as safety issues are debated and security concerns raised.

Biometric systems are available and are being advanced rapidly with faster computers and better operating software. These technologies are being demanded by law enforcement agencies while caution is being raised by civil libertarians and others. These concerns are not being raised in the traditional liberal corner of American politics but are being raised by conservatives as well transcending traditional political boundaries. The issues of privacy, liberty and freedom cross all sectors of civil society – republican, democrat or independent.

"Biometric identification techniques using unique biological characteristics such as fingerprints or iris patterns are now falling into commercial use. The recent decrease in price for such technology has allowed biometric identification systems to be used in two main areas: banking and governmental agencies. For banks, the use of the technology is more for the sake of convenience than security, as the customer does not need an ATM pin number, but rather just needs to stare into a camera.

While this technology may stop a thief from guessing a pin number, it cannot stop holdups at ATMs. However, for governmental agencies, the technology has more of a security application, as it makes false identities easy to detect. Some states use biometrics to ascertain the identity of welfare recipients, and the Department of Defense and the Department of Veterans Affairs are both currently investigating the use of fingerprinting for identification purposes for employees and for those attempting to receive benefits. However, biometric technology has come under fire from privacy groups and civil libertarians, who claim that the technology will allow undemocratic governments to repress citizens and track dissidents. Opponents say that those

285 Simson, Garfinkel. *(Toronto Star)*, "Reading Your Body." Oct. 2, 2000. *Law Enforcement & Corrections Technology News Summary*, Oct. 12, 2000. EPI2927

with unpopular views in authoritarian countries, as well as those who need to change identities in order to escape a stalker or abuser, have found false identification papers to be essential for survival in the past. Critics contend that if the government can absolutely identify everyone in the population, then complete control is possible. The specter of hackers breaking into a database where the IDs are stored is also a frightening prospect, say critics. These negative consequences are part of the reason Congress has consistently voted against the idea of a universally required ID card, and even proponents of the technology say that it is unlikely that the entire population of the United States will be required to have some sort of biometric identification. However, most analysts contend that some part of the population, most likely the poor who collect welfare and immigrants, will fall under biometric identification requirements, thereby missing out on the the privacy protections given to the rest of society." 286

The leading United States manufacturers of these technologies are exporting them into countries where public opinion is discounted and not regarded in the decision making process. China, as well as other developing countries, are significant consumers of this technology and are provided a "testbed" for the further expansion of the technology globally for military, political and commercial purposes. "The company that supplied controversial face recognition technology to scan people on the streets of Tampa, Fla., is working with commercial partners in China to supply the same technology there. Joseph Atick, Chairman and CEO of Visionics Corp. and an inventor of face recognition technology, told reporters Wednesday that his company is doing business in roughly 50 to 60 nations, including China."287 Why is the United States allowing the export of these technologies to governments who will surely use them for purposes most would find objectionable. It was US systems which were in place in China when pro-democracy protests occurred in the 1990s resulting in hundreds of arrests in China of people fighting for basic civil rights and fundamental democratic principles.

---

286 *Industrial Physicist*. "Biometric Identification." *Law Enforcement & Corrections Technology News Summary*, March 30, 2000. EPI2021

287 Divis, Dee Ann. *(UPI)*. "Face-scan technology selling in China." Aug. 9, 2001. *www.vny.com* EPI3539

The problem with each of these systems is that they will catalog huge amounts of information which could be subject to misuse by those with access to the data. Moreover, hacking remains a concern to people following these issues because as the information is stored, it is also subject to tampering. This is further brought out in the writings regarding future wars and conflicts where information systems are some of the prime targets for any would-be adversary taking on superpowers in the 21st century.

In order to provide the sense of security held by the public these new systems will continue to be advanced starting with identification cards and likely ending with implantable technologies. In the past when implants were suggested in any public announcements they were strongly resisted by public opinion – not so any longer. These systems are being used for animals in identifying them and are being suggested for children or the elderly who may have memory difficulties, again playing on fear, to motivate people in this area.

Implants – The Technology of Today

"The implant technology is another case of science fiction evolving into fact. Those who have long advanced the idea of implant chips say it could someday mean no more easy-to-counterfeit ID cards nor dozing security guards. Just a computer chip – about the size of a grain of rice – that would be difficult to remove and tough to mimic."[288] Associated Press stories and news releases have increasingly discussed these technologies. The most common markets or targets for the technology are prisoners, military service personnel, children, elderly persons and visitors to the United States.

"A Florida technology company is poised to ask the government to market a first-ever computer ID chip that could be imbedded beneath a person's skin. For airports, nuclear power plants, and other high security facilities, the immediate benefits would be a closer-to-foolproof security system. But privacy advocates warn the chip could lead to encroachments on civil

288 Newton, Christopher. *(AP)*. "ID chips sure to get under skin." Feb. 27, 2002. *Anchorage Daily News* EPI3885

liberties."289 With the announcement regulatory agencies are already providing the regulatory green light for these new systems. "The Federal Food and Drug Administration has ruled that an implantable microchip used for ID purposes is not a regulated device, paving the way for the chip's immediate sale in the United States, the manufacturer announced today." 290

Some devices are used for tracking a person's movements and monitoring body functions at the same time. "Integrated microsystems are being developed at UM that can be implanted in the human body to eavesdrop on what's going on with various biological functions, interpret the informa-tion, and treat any existing disorder using chemical or electrical stimuli delivered at the cellular level." 291

"The Digital Angel® system makes use of the Global Positioning System's network of satellites to figure out the chip's position. On-board biometric technology is capable of monitoring vital statistics such as body temperature, pulse rate and blood pressure. This information is then relayed via another GPS signal or a wireless communications system to a remote monitoring system. The whole system is powered by body heat, so the chip doesn't have any batteries that need replacing." 292 Batteries biologically included as humans become the power source for their own enslavement.

"Applied Digital Solutions, Inc. today announced that it has acquired the patent rights to a miniature transceiver – which it has named 'Digital Angel®' – that can be used for a variety of purposes, such as providing a tamperproof means of identification for enhanced e-business security, locating lost or missing individuals, tracking the location of valuable property and monitoring the medical conditions of at-risk patients. The implantable transceiver sends and receives data and can be

289 Newton, Christopher. *(AP)*. "US to Weigh Computer Chip Implant." Feb. 26, 2002. EPI3864

290 Scheeres, Julia. *(Wired News)*. "Why, Hello Mr. Chips." April 4, 2002. *wirednews.com* EPI3928

291 *RF Globalnet*. "Michigan College of Engineering Becomes First Engineering Research Center for Wireless Integrated Microsystems." Sept. 19, 2000. EPI3245

292 Della Bitta, Michael. "Digital Angel: The New Eye in the Sky." *foxnews.com*, Oct. 16, 2000. EPI2840

continuously tracked by GPS technology."[293] Geographical Positioning Systems (GPS) are used for locating property or people with a high degree of accuracy. These systems were first used by the military and then installed on commercial vehicles for tracing freight flows. These GPS systems are now being considered for people. These systems will become even more powerful as the technology advances and it is further miniaturized..

These systems have already evolved so that the same sized device of a few years ago can now keep track of vital functions of the body, monitor stress levels, chemicals in the body and other parameters of life. In the future as circuits become smaller, more powerful in their multifaceted uses and cheaper to produce additional advances will be made. It is anticipated that these technologies may one day be used for conducting all secured business transactions replacing cash and other forms of identification. Security issues will continue to drive the process. Already, according to the United States Federal Trade Commission, identity theft is the fastest growing crime in America. The issue of identity theft will continue to increase racking up financial losses for banks and corporations leading first to more secure credit cards and then, in the future, implants for use in official identification, tracking individual persons and then full integration into society. These "convenient" systems will one day provide a matrix for manipulation which will lead to the "more controlled and directed society" that writers and researchers warned about in the last century. "1984" was a few decades late in its predictions but is now well on its way to the reality present in the opening years of this new century.

Smart Cards or Intrusion?

Banking security is something most people understand and hear about often. Already added into the advertising mix for ATT and banks is the idea of smart cards that are read based on radio signals generated by these new devices. What this allows for is tracing not just transactions but also the movement of people within stores or larger areas. "US bank-issued smart cards for mobile/e-commerce applications are one step closer to reality thanks to an initiative by MasterCard International. The

293 Applied Digital Solutions, Inc. "Applied Digital Solutions Acquires Rights to World's First Digital Device." Company Press Release, Dec. 15, 1999. EPI1296

bank card issuer has gathered a coalition of smart card developers, terminal vendors and security providers to develop standard interoperable solutions for digital ID-based smart cards. Its aim is to migrate MasterCard International's 22,000 member banks to digital ID-based smart cards that incorporate identifying codes, personal identification numbers or biometrics data to authenticate and identify card users." 294 Pressure will increase for wider use of these systems by banks and credit card companies as they try to reduce losses caused by fraud. Failure to accept these technologies will result in a segmented market where those that first take the devices will be given greater security in that losses will go to the credit card companies and banks whereas those that do not use the technology might be responsible for their own losses. What choice will people make, when it is increasingly difficult to gain access to the economic system unless an individual is willing to sacrifice the legitimate levels of privacy for increased government and corporate control of our lives. We expect this to be a gradual change as fear, insecurity and wishful thinking overshadow privacy as an issue of common concern.

Meanwhile the fear mounts and good sense evaporates. We always target the few in introducing the population to accept what would otherwise be questioned by most thinking people. "Saying the nation needs to secure its borders to keep future terrorists out of the country, two key US senators announced today they would introduce far-reaching legislation to require millions of foreigners to carry 'biometric smart visa' cards to travel to the United States. The cards, which work like credit cards, would contain fingerprints and other personal information, according to the measure proposed by Sen. Jon Kyl, R-Ariz., and Sen. Diane Feinstine, D-Calif."295 Politicians echo what they believe the public wants when gauging their pronouncements. Tracking sex offenders and convicted felons will likely be subject to implantation as well as a way of hanging an electronic "scarlet letter" or a "yellow star" for ease of identification. Eventually, pressure will mount for all people to be treated in the same way – adding implants in exchange for political, economic and social access.

---

294 Quan, Margaret. *(EE Times)*. "MasterCard leads coalition to spur smart card use." *edtn.com*, Aug. 30, 2000. EPI2399

295 Bustos, Sergio. *(Gannett News Service)*. "Kyl proposes 'smart' ID card for immigration." Oct. 25, 2001. *www.arizonarepublic.com* EPI3707

In something that was unthinkable before New York's terrorist attack the congress weighed-in with a sweeping exchange of privacy for security. "Tucked quietly into the counterterrorism package that President Bush signed into law is a measure that could require foreigners to use identification cards to enter the United States. Identification cards would be developed through 'biometric' technology; the law also recommends production of 'tamper-resistant' passports."[296] This represents a first step in a direction which is a slippery slope.

New Military Identification

We reported in 1995[297] that the military think tanks were considering the use of implant technologies and smart cards for several different purposes. In these early reports it was also clear in the military writings that these technologies would be challenged by the public as they moved forward unless introduced on a foundation of fear. That fear, it was predicted, would be based on international terrorism and drug trafficking. It took eight years and an attack on New York to bring this into reality and set the stage for huge changes in society – the betrayal begins.

In the case of military personnel the use of an implant for locating personnel in the battlefield and monitoring their vital functions has become important. This system would allow for tracking our own troop movements and might also allow a sophisticated adversary the capacity to pinpoint our personnel as well. What many forget is that a system only stays advanced a short time in terms of world developments. Where the United States and a few other governments may be ahead today, they can just as easily be behind in the evolution of counter measures. Technology is widespread and innovation is possible in all human beings. Who will be the first Iraq, Russia, China or someone else? Who will be the last? Most importantly, will these systems serve human interests or violate the very essence of who we are?

The first round of release of smart cards was in late 2001 with more planned in the near term. "The card – with two photos,

296 Boyer, Dave. *(Washington Times)*. "New law contains ID-card proposal." Nov. 1, 2001. *www.washingtontimes.com* EPI3739

297 *Angels Don't Play this HAARP*, Begich & Manning, Earthpulse Press Incorporated, September 1995.

two bar codes, a magnetic strip and the etched gold chip, looks like a driver's license on steroids. More than 120,000 active duty military personnel, selected reserves, Defense Department civilians and some contractors have received the cards in recent months. About 4 million are to be issued over the next two years."298 "The Pentagon plans to issue 4 million or more high-tech identification cards to soldiers and other personnel worldwide, hoping to provide better security for access to bases, buildings and computer systems. The new 'common access card' contains a tiny computer chip, using 'smart card' technology to store and process a myriad of information. Similar technology has been used by smaller governments, including Spain and Finland, and in commercial operations." 299

"The ActivCard software provides simultaneous and secure connections to two independently managed systems from which user applications and data are acquired. The first system is the DMDC's Defense Enrollment Eligibility Reporting System (DEERS), containing information on over 23 million people. The second system is the Defense Information Systems Agency's (DISA) PKI Certificate Management System. The end result is a system that is deployed worldwide to issue CAC ID badges to all DoD employees and contractors. The new badges will support a wide range of functionality from building access to financial services to digital identity for access to government services and information containing personnel information and processing credentials that enable digital signature, encryption, and strong user authentication." 300 "Among the add-on functions being mulled [for ActivCard DOD badges] are processing food service charges in military mess halls...Local commands are looking at putting individual medical and dental information on the card along with details on training and rifle range performance, officials told a news briefing." September, 2002, is the target date for the initial issuance, including active duty military, selected reserve forces, civilian employees of the Pentagon and eligible contractors. 301

298 O'Harrow Jr. et al. *(Washington Post)*. "Weapon against terror: the ID card." Dec. 23, 2001. *Anchorage Daily News* EPI3814

299 *AP*. "Pentagon Introduces High-Tech ID." Oct. 10, 2000. EPI2695

300 ActivCard, Inc. "ActivCard Wins Department of Defense (DOD) Project." *PR Newswire*, Oct. 10, 2000. EPI2694

301 Wolf, Jim. *(Reuters)*. "Pentagon Launches 'Smart Card' ID Badge." Oct. 10, 2000. EPI2696

We believe that the next generation of implant technology is now approaching based on the state of the technology already being used in selected environments. We expect that these technologies are already in use with Special Forces and other high priority missions where risk assessment and location is critical. In reflecting on this possibility, if I were in the armed services, would I want an implant? Perhaps if I were in combat I would want this additional device as a way to be found if wounded, lost or captured. The decision however would not be mine but the military's under the conditions of military service which raises additional questions as to who is responsible for what goes under an individual's skin – the individual or the government?

Snooper Bowl

Compared to implants other systems seemed to pale in comparison yet these systems need to be considered. This years Super Bowl (2003) was spared the use of facial recognition cameras with the CNN aired excuse that the technology was in need of advancement to be refined enough for this use, while the real reason was public concern about privacy. This we interpreted as a good thing as the public was heard on this issue but only because it got public attention. In other parts of the world this is not the case.

In 2001 the public was the target in a test of these facial recognition technologies. "When police used secret cameras to scan the faces of 100,000 people at the Super Bowl, they appeared to be fulfilling a longtime goal to rapidly identify criminals in a crowd. But worries about the invasion of privacy may be premature because the technology is still far from foolproof and not yet widely used. Experts warn that covert digital facial scans can be highly unreliable in public settings because digitalized photos shot at an angle or in poor light create images that often fail to match existing mug shots." 302 "Super Bowl fans never knew it, but police video cameras focused on their faces, one by one, as they streamed through the turnstiles in Tampa on Sunday. Cables instantly carried the images to computers, which spent less than a second comparing them with thousands of digital portraits of known criminals and suspected terrorists. The extraordinary test of technology during the highest-profile US sporting event of

302 Piller et al. "Criminal Faces in the Crowd Still Elude Hidden ID Cameras." *latimes.com*, Feb. 2, 2001. EPI3012

the year yielded one hit, a ticket scalper who vanished into the crowd, reported an official at the company that installed the cameras." 303

"Facial recognition technology is still a fairly small industry, and its reliability is still being questioned. According to Jim Wayman, director of San Jose State University's Biometric Test Center, laboratory test results indicate that the technology is not effective for more than a 'rough filtering' of suspects. A recent study done by the National Institute of Standards and Technology demonstrated a 43 percent false rejection rate by the computer of same suspect photos taken 18 months apart. A similar test with substantially identical results is forthcoming from the Defense Department. At the recent Super Bowl in Tampa, Fla., police used Graphco Technology to secretly scan the faces of 100,000 spectators and were able to identify 19 people who, when crosschecked to data files, did have criminal histories. Prior to the testing at the Super Bowl, Tampa police had given Graphco a databank of 1,700 people who had criminal records stemming from ticket scalping and fraud to violent crimes. Las Vegas casinos are also using the new technology, but one software manufacturer, Images Technologies, has already cautioned them about the effectiveness being compromised by casino lighting. To effectively identify someone inside a casino is a challenge, not only because of the lighting, but also because of camera angles. Experts recommend that cameras need to be developed that have a 360-degree rotation flexibility and the capability to rapidly zoom in on targets. Many communities are using the technology to snap photos of traffic violators, then mail the person a ticket, or they use it to observe crowds in the town's more commercial places. While there are some who might feel that the covert nature of the technology violates personal rights, Michael D. Brasfield, the chief of police in Fort Lauderdale, Fla., believes that 'any technology that can enhance public safety but not violate the individual rights of citizens is worth pursuing.'" 304 What did he say? Do these individuals understand what privacy is in the real world of modern technology?

---

303 Slevin, Peter. *(Washington Post)*. "Police Video Cameras Taped Football Fans." *washingtonpost.com*, Feb. 1, 2001. EPI2996

304 Piller et al. *(Los Angeles Times)*. "Criminal Faces in the Crowd Still Elude Hidden ID Cameras." Feb. 2, 2001. *Law Enforcement & Corrections Technology News Summary*, Feb. 8, 2001. EPI3064

"'If the public doesn't object to what happened at the 'Snooper Bowl,' then the authorities will certainly feel emboldened to move us down the road to total surveillance,' said the ACLU's Howard Simon."305 This assessment was right on target when the larger issues were considered and has helped slow the direction of the technology.

Political leaders also began to assess the technology in light of the general direction and long term effects of these innovations. "Sen. Chris Dodd, D-Conn., who is weighing new federal privacy rights legislation as a member of the Congressional privacy caucus, said the Super Bowl monitoring was the latest example of a steady erosion of privacy rights. 'It's come to the point where even attending something as innocuous as a sporting event can result in people's private information – without any consent, any knowledge beforehand – being collected and gathered,' said Dodd. 'This is an issue that transcends politics, and ideology and partisanship.'" 306 We were heartened in that the issue was being raised but like all issues of this magnitude the follow-up work is required or the public concern dies down and the systems move forward.

The Olympics were the next event where these kinds of systems were installed and used. "Boca Raton, Fla., based Sensormatic Electronics Corporation has deployed some 260 high-tech cameras to Salt Lake City, Utah, to be used for safety and precautionary purposes at the Salt Lake City Winter Olympic Games in 2002. The company says it has installed the first of the cameras, which can magnify an image up to 176 times – zooming to the point where the name on an athlete's helmet can be discerned – at the bobsled and luge racetrack. A spokeswoman for Sensormatic said the company has been asked only to provide the equipment and that Olympic organizers would handle all programming and operational responsibilities. The cameras will have built-in heaters, in order to withstand the brutal cold of the Utah winter, and they will be installed throughout the Athlete's Village and at other key venues. In other news, the Sensormatic spokeswoman said controversial face-recognition technology that

305 Chachere, Vickie. "Super Security Makes Some Nervous." *AP*, Feb. 11, 2001. EPI3047

306 Gay, Lance. *(Scripps Howard News Service)*. "Cameras, cameras everywhere." Feb. 1, 2001. EPI3048

was used at the Super Bowl in January would not be employed for the Olympic Games. The technology drew the ire of the American Civil Liberties Union, which claimed it '[raised] concerns about the (constitutional) right of all citizens to be free of unreasonable searches and seizures.'" 307

Facial & Other Recognition Systems

"Surveillance cameras often capture a criminal act but produce pictures too fuzzy for the perpetrator to be identified. New software developed by doctoral student James Robinson at Staffordshire University in the U.K. could tighten up this hole in the law enforcement apparatus. The software stitches together several of the blurry still-frame images that have been captured on security camera film and creates a three-dimensional model of the mischief-maker's face." 308 This breakthrough will continue to make facial recognition systems even more useful in their various application by improving accuracy.

"ILEFIS is the next-generation face-identification system, designed specifically for use by local, State, and Federal law enforcement organizations. It is based on a framework for rendering faces (heads) in three dimensions (3-D) utilizing existing 2-D face images (a frontal view and a profile view) of arrested persons currently maintained in local, State, and Federal mugshot depositories. ILEFIS is being developed as the critically needed robust face-identification technology that will overtake the existing technologies in recognition of angled-view images associated with all current face-recognition technologies. It is designed to run on low- to moderate- cost PC platforms, nationally integrated as a network of ILEFIS station servers installed in local, State, and Federal law enforcement organizations. Each ILEFIS station server is designed to have the capability to locally store, maintain, and process encoded information about the available mugshot data files and the associated records (e.g., arrests), estimated as more than 60 million, which is increasing at a rate of 20 million new mugshots per year in the United States." 309

307 *Agence France Presse.* "High-Tech Cameras to Be Used for Security at Salt Lake Games." Feb. 7, 2001. *Law Enforcement & Corrections Technology News Summary,* Feb. 15, 2001. EPI3057

308 *Technology Review,* "Mug Shot Maker." July/Aug 2000. EPI2632

309 Justice Technology Information Network (JUSTNET). Project Status Report: Integrated Law Enforcement Face-Identification System (ILEFIS). May 11, 1999. http://www.nlectc.org/techproj/ EPI2945

Visionics Corporation continues to be one of the leaders in this area. "A company that touts its facial identification system as a powerful new tool for security and crime fighting has received millions of dollars in federal funding to improve its surveillance technology for military and intelligence uses, according to documents and interviews. Visionics Corp. of Jersey City, N.J. specializes in systems that use cameras linked to computers to scan faces and automatically compare them with electronic photographs stored in databases."310 These technologies are not just for intelligence gathering but are also for civilian projects.

In Florida these systems are not just being used for military but are also being used for other law enforcement activities. "So far, police in Tampa have made no arrests based on the face-scanning software. But officials in the East London borough of Newham, where 250 cameras installed by Visionics have scanned pedestrians for the past three years, insist that law-abiding citizens have nothing to fear. The technology, says town official Bob Lack, is not Big Brother, but more like 'a friendly uncle and aunt watching over you.'"311 Nothing like a friendly uncle or aunt....?

Great Britain tends to be the most advanced in these technologies for civilian purposes in law enforcement. Already in Europe face recognition technology is being used to identify known football hooligans with a history of inciting violence at sporting events. "Visionics Corporation announced that its world leading automated facial recognition technology engine, FaceIt®, was used in a successful operation to identify known football – or soccer, as the game is called in the US – hooligans congregating in areas close to the stadium during a recent high-profile match." 312

These systems have been added to the streets of British cities and are increasing in use as terror and fear increasingly

310 O'Harrow Jr., Robert. *(Washington Post).* "Matching Faces With Mug Shots." Aug. 1, 2001. *washingtonpost.com* EPI3517

311 Wakefield, Julie. "A Face in the Crowd." November/December 2001. *Mother Jones* EPI3763

312 Visionics Corporation. "FaceIt(R) Successfully Deployed by London's Metropolitan Police Service at Recent Football Match." Press Release, Jan. 10, 2000. EPI2571

dominate the emotions of individuals and governments. "The London Borough of Newham has won a bid to upgrade its Closed Circuit Television (CCTV) anti-crime application that uses Visionics' FaceIt® facial recognition software. The award is an extension of the British government's crime reduction program started in July 1998. The FaceIt® software automatically scans the faces of people passing the network of 250 cameras placed around Newham. The faces are then searched for those of known criminals, and law enforcement is alerted to any matches. Malcolm Smith, Council Director in charge of the Newham CCTV system, states that the software has maximized efficiency, and reduced crime and antisocial behavior. Visionics has since introduced the third generation FaceIt® engine, in an attempt to stay ahead of the competition. Newham has reported a nearly 70 percent reduction in crime in the18 months since FaceIt® began." 313

The institutions which deal with this kind of issue have been slow to act and are not, in our opinion, keeping abreast of these issues as they emerge in their earliest development. As a result, they enter the debate after the first battles for public acceptability have been fought. Increased diligence in research and engaging public discussion is required and these efforts must be sustained to be effective in stemming the tide of these developments. Visionics Corporation continues to spread the word and release information which capitalizes on the environment of fear present throughout the country. "An artificial intelligence program called FaceIt, developed by Visionics Corp. of Jersey City, N.J., can copy the way a human brain sees the face and compare the landmarks it views to the faces in a database of recorded images. Each face is different, and the relationship between the landmarks makes a map that the program can distinguish. But while face recognition may be great for identification and privacy, its potential use in surveillance is disconcerting; the technology's ability to monitor the movements of a specific person hint at Big Brother. The American Civil Liberties Union, among other activist groups, is beginning to explore the problems associated with face recognition. But it lends itself to tracking the normal, everyday activities of innocent members of

313 *Business Wire*. "Government Awards London Borough With Major Grant to Expand CCTV Surveillance program." *Law Enforcement & Corrections Technology News Summary*, Feb. 10, 2000. EPI2052

society by public and private groups. In Newham, a section in East London, face recognition technology has already led to a reduction in the crime rate by checking faces that go past the cameras in the neighborhood against a database of criminals' images. The borough has received more funding from the government for increased use, but advocates say the technology is harmless to innocent people, deleting recorded images that will not match any in its database. But the ACLU, among others, would like better regulation; it says the potential applications for misuse are tremendous." 314

Use of these systems for computer terminal access seems to be one of those uses that could meet with widespread acceptance and may prove to be one of the best ways to protect a commercial or home computer. "Face recognition is the only biometric that can be used in two modalities – logon and continuous monitoring. The first is [a] perimeter defense mechan-ism; an authorized individual gains entry to a network or session after a one-time logon process. Thereafter, the system usually does not offer any authentication. With FaceIt®, users can be continuously authenticated ensuring that at all times, the individual in front of the computer or hand-held device continues to be the same authorized person who logged on." 315 The important aspect of all technologies are not their actual uses but the intent and will of the individuals operating these systems. The very same systems used for degrading privacy can often be used for enhancing privacy thus amplifying basic civil standards of what is right and wrong in this area.

"FaceIt® will automatically capture faces in the field of view, extract them from their background and compare them against a watchlist or database of certain individuals. These could be shoplifters, known terrorists or criminals, VIP guests or customers, expected visitors or any individuals generally classified as friends or foes. This automated system can be used at airports, casinos, public buildings, schools, subways, colleges, factories, business facilities, housing complexes, residences, etc." 316 Again these uses raise the issue of how this information might

314 *Montreal Gazette.* "The End of Passwords? Digital-Imaging Technology Will Allow Machines to Recognize Your Face." *Law Enforcement & Corrections Technology News Summary,* March 9, 2000. EPI2026

315 Visionics Corporation. "Authentication." www.faceit.com EPI2573

316 Visionics Corporation. "Human ID at a Distance" www.faceit.com EPI2793

soon be used. These smart systems will change the way information is utilized and services delivered throughout society. Society will change as the technologies are advanced into one with high levels of transparency and increased information. The use of information to influence political outcomes, consumer choices or other decisions we make as individuals, and as larger populations, will be the target of these new technologies.

"By conducting searches against facial images, FaceIt® yields instant results, verifying the identity of a suspect instantly and checking through millions of records for possible matches quickly, automatically and reliably. No other technology gives law enforcement the ability to identify suspects without their active participation." 317 While the claims of the corporations who are advancing the technology outstrip the current reality the ability to reach these claims will soon be realized as massive research dollars flow to this sector. These technologies are being sought as the high-tech tools of political control. The important issues will be centered on who will access the technologies, for what purposes and when will they be used?

The greater advances in the technology offer users even more possibilities than just face recognition. These technologies will also interpret a person's movements to determine if they are within normal ranges of activity. The "new technology may allow machines to watch for 'abnormal' behavior and alert security personnel to crimes before they are even committed. A prototype of this technology has been developed by Steve Maybank at the University of Reading and David Hogg at the University of Leeds. The research was developed as a way to cut down on car theft in parking lots. A computer was programmed under the notion that most people behave in predictable ways when walking to their car, in a not-so predictable as to be a mathematical pattern, and the computer recognizes it as such. The computer also recognizes basic shapes, such as cars and people. Anyone who deviates from this set pattern, such as someone who walks in circles or who lurks in shadows, will set off an alarm, which can prompt security personnel to investigate. Operators of this technology can change the definition of 'normal behavior' by changing the 'threshold value' of factors, such as walking speed.

317 Visionics Corporation. "Criminal Justice Systems." www.faceit.com EPI2574

However, this technology not only spots car thieves, but any behavior that is aberrant, such as a fist fight. Another technology called Cromatica was recently developed in London to monitor the subway system there. The system alerts personnel to dangerous crowd levels, abnormal behavior, and most remarkably, those attempting to commit suicide by jumping in front of a train. The researchers analyzed previous suicide attempts and programmed the computer to watch for such behavior as waiting at least 10 minutes on the platform and letting several trains go by. In trial runs, Cromatica spotted 98 percent of the events that were seen by security personnel, and only rang a false alarm 1 percent of the time. Despite the good such technology may be able to do, privacy advocates are deeply concerned about it. They wonder who will define 'normal behavior', and worry that anyone who does not conform to the most rigid standards of acceptable conduct will be apprehended and questioned by security guards. They say that this would have the effect of making society completely conformist, like something out of '1984.' Regardless, surveillance experts say that no matter how the technology is used, surveillance equipment will get much smarter in the near future, and become more proactive instead of reactive."[318] This technology is now three years old and has already advanced into these proactive areas of use by anticipating human behavior.

While accuracy continues to be a problem these systems are quickly evolving under priority funding throughout the world. Safety and security is the trade-off in all of these new breakthroughs. The right use of science and technology remains in the forefront of many of us as we attempt to see the future based on the state of present technologies.

"AuthenTec recently unveiled a new chip that recognizes fingerprints and is expected to be integrated into the products of computer makers, cell phone companies, and other hardware manufacturers. The technology, backed by 36 patents, could be used to start computers or access sensitive e-mails or Web sites, including online bank accounts. Corporations could also use finger scanning to save money on password maintenance, and could employ the scanners in lieu of keys or number combinations to limit access to buildings and rooms. Biometric Group

---

318 *New Scientist.* "Warning! Strange Behavior." *Law Enforcement & Corrections Technology News Summary,* Jan. 6, 2000. EPI2009

says sales of hardware and software that use unique physical characteristics to identify users will jump from $58.4 million in 1999 to $594 million in 2003, with finger scanning comprising 46 percent of the biometric market share by 2003, up from its current 34 percent. As the size of scanners get smaller, prices go down, and accuracy increases, they will become much more attractive to corporations, experts say." 319

Insecurity has opened new markets which were expected to grow 1000% in the ten years between 1993 and 2003. What was not expected was September 11, 2001, when the world was forever changed. Growth in this areas has mushroomed in the aftermath and continues to accelerate as reality is lost in a sea of fear.

Integration of technology starts at a young age. Starting this fall, some students will buy their lunch simply by looking at a web camera in the school cafeteria and saying their name, thanks to a food service company that is tapping face and voice recognition technology. BioID's biometric authentication software recognizes a user's face, voice, and lip movement simultaneously."320 The use of these technologies in young populations establishes acceptance so that as these systems integrate into society – people view them as useful and convenient rather than intrusive.

DNA Identification

The ultimate identification system will combine biometric data with other information for secure communications and interactions of all kinds whether commercial, military or private. DNA offers the most significant change and place where abuse can occur by making available the literal physical blueprint to our individual makeup as a living soul. Is DNA a matter of privacy?

Police, when asked the question in Great Britain, raised deep concerns where it might impact them. In a race to invade the privacy of others and faced with the same issues personally, a much different response occurred. The same happened in the

319 Williams, Molly. *(Wall Street Journal)*. "AuthenTec Sees Wide Use for Fingerprint ID." Dec. 14, 2000. *Law Enforcement & Corrections Technology News Summary*, Dec. 21, 2000. EPI2930

320 Branigan, Cara. "Students face controversial new lunch-line technology." July 24, 2001. *www.eschoolnews.com* EPI3493

United States in the case of federal employees who's genetic information was protected by an Executive Order issued by then President Bill Clinton. The rest of the US population was not protected by the order and remain largely unprotected by law from abuse of information. In Great Britain "Thousands of police officers have refused to give DNA samples to a new Home Office database amid concerns that the genetic fingerprints could be used against them in paternity suits. Police officers are also said to be anxious that their samples could be used to check for drugs, but their big concern is that the Child Support Agency will be able to access the computer database in a bid to track down fathers who shirk their responsibility." 321

While the US is well aware of the privacy issues, the security issues are taking precedence. "Privacy concerns over the use of biometrics technology to secure data may lead the Defense Department to change how that information is labeled and handled – by tagging biometrics data as personal information protected under the Freedom of Information Act. The technology is increasingly being considered, especially by the Pentagon, for protecting physical facilities and information networks." 322 As each system is brought on line it is our prediction that the systems will be violated and hacked through resulting in increased security systems which will likely end with the most intrusive being evolved – implantable "tamper proof" technologies.

The US at least has some constitutional provisions which can limit here what is happening in other parts of the world. Again Great Britain figures into the debate as Americans are reminded again two hundred years later why we left Europe – it was for freedom, privacy in religion and avoiding torture with its outcome self-incrimination. "Drivers or other people stopped by police could be asked to supply on-the-spot hair or saliva samples to identify whether they are wanted criminals. Government scientists have developed a hand-held DNA testing kit to be carried and operated by police officers during regular patrols. The device would be electronically linked to the national DNA database, which Tony Blair has hailed as an essential tool in the fight

321 Taylor, David. *(Daily Express)*. "Worried police refuse to give DNA samples." July 2, 2000. www.lineone.net/express EPI2549
322 Seffers, George. *(Federal Computer Week)*. "The details are in the bio." *fcw.com*, April 30, 2001. EPI3202

against crime. The Forensic Science Service will disclose to Parliament this week that the equipment could be ready for standard use within a couple of years." 323

These systems are intended to open a person's entire life to public scrutiny. "The system in Northern Ireland is to penetrate your target's entire life. That's fine if you're stopping bombers. But the surveillance machine, for want of employment, is now increasingly being turned on Britons at home. The British population is now the most intensely surveilled in the world. The terrorist's loss of privacy is progressing to the ordinary citizen's."324 This loss of privacy has collapsed most systems once thought by civilized people to be fundamental to basic human rights – the right to a private life.

How far are we from these kinds of intrusions? We again only have to look across the sea to Europe. "The prospect of routine DNA screening of the entire population drew nearer yesterday when the Government proposed to give the police the power to retain indefinitely samples taken from innocent people. The proposal forms the centerpiece of the Criminal Justice and Police Bill, which also provides for a significant extension of police powers to control the streets and seize property. The bill gives the police new powers to seize documents and computer discs even if they contain privileged legal information."325 It will be security issues and public fear which allow for these changes in personal privacy in the United States as well.

The United States already has a great deal of raw material to draw from in setting up such a system of DNA monitoring. "One major source of DNA is in the form of blood taken from newborns to check for genetic diseases. Since the mid-1960s, the blood has been dried on 'Guthrie cards' and stored in state laboratories. Some keep the cards for a few weeks, others up to 25 years. DNA samples are also taken from military recruits. According to the Coast Guard website, samples are stored for 50 years, and DNA tests are conducted only to identify a soldier's body. A third major source is the FBI's Combined DNA Index

323 Cracknell, David. "Roadside DNA tests planned." *www.telegraph.co.uk*, Dec. 10, 2000. EPI3074

324 Lewis, Anthony. "Big Brother Pounces." *New York Times*, Dec. 7, 1999. EPI1300

325 Johnston, Philip. "Police to get new powers on DNA testing." *www.telegraph.co.uk*, Jan. 20, 2001. EPI3075

System (CODIS), which compiles DNA profiles of people convicted of felonies and from evidence collected at crime scenes."[326] Community or even countrywide typing and sampling is increasingly proposed by governments around the world.

"The scientist who discovered genetic fingerprinting wants the entire population of Britain to be DNA tested to try to combat serious crime. Professor Sir Alec Jeffreys, who devised the system to identify criminals from the unique characteristics of their genes, said that he had changed his mind about the human rights implications of a universal DNA database."[327] Politicians also press for these issues to become realities in modern society effectively lowering the bar on personal information which will be kept on people. What are the limits and where it will end depends on the political process and its effectiveness. Change is required but those changes should be driven by rightly placed values rather than fear. "A politician's suggestion to take mandatory DNA samples from Australians at birth was described as police state tactics by a civil libertarian today. Federal Liberal MP Peter Lindsay has called for mandatory DNA samples to be taken from all Australians, starting with newborn babies, to further empower law enforcement agencies in view of the growing incidence of crime in Australia." [328]

"Every time the police take a saliva or blood sample for DNA fingerprinting they are unknowingly collecting potentially sensitive genetic information concerning the health of the suspects they are testing. A British team has discovered that the standard DNA fingerprints used by police around the world contain a subtle signature which can be linked to a person's susceptibility to type 1 diabetes."[329] More will likely be discovered as well and time, public opinion and the political will of the population effected will dictate its use.

---

326 Hembree, Amy. "ID, Registration and DNA, Please." *www.wired.com,* Feb. 26, 2001. EPI3079

327 *Electronic Telegraph.* "DNA tests for all will cut crime, says pioneer." *www.telegraph.co.uk,* Feb. 19, 2001. EPI3131

328 *AAP.* "Rights group slams plans for DNA database." April 26, 2001. www.theage.com.au EPI3253

329 Concar, David. "Fingerprint fear: DNA fingerprints used by police contain information about the health of the suspect, with huge ethical implications." *newscientist.com,* May 2, 2001. EPI3281

During the aftermath of the attack on New York much was made of the use of DNA in identifying people in the rubble. Yet the real effectiveness was shown for its inability to meet the needs of the situation without advance samples from the victims of the disaster. "After Sept. 11, thousands of items were collected from families who lost relatives in the World Trade Center attack, in a hurried and often scattershot effort to help identify remains. But now the New York City medical examiner's office says that more than half of the possible DNA samples it has received are inadequate to make such matches."[330] Even with limited success the hope of using genetic information remained of interest for identifying our dead as well as our adversaries. "The government is seeking samples of DNA from Osama bin Laden's family to determine if human remains found in Afghanistan belong to the terrorist leader, law enforcement and other US officials said Wednesday. In theory, it wouldn't take much of a sample. A blood specimen, a scraping from inside of the mouth, even a hair follicle could provide enough DNA for a match." [331]

More Developments

"Biometrics technology, for years an authentication solution in search of a problem, is now chasing a new market: online exchanges. Because no two people have the same fingerprints, some observers see the process of scanning fingers, a form of biometrics, as perhaps the most secure means of authentication. Although the technology is unproven and some question whether users will be comfortable with the technology, there have been several key technological advances and pilots."[332] This system for accessing a computer, making a handgun fire, or even opening your home or automobile door have been suggested. Some of these uses have great value as security measures but are subject to abuse and technical malfunction. The issues again surround what is fair or reasonable use – standards which are forever shifting but are already being promoted by such companies as IBM for secure home and business computers.

330 Chen, David W. *(New York Times)*. "Reopening wounds." Feb. 17, 2002. *Anchorage Daily News* EPI3826

331 Lumpkin, John J. *(AP)*. "US needs bin Laden DNA sample." Feb. 28, 2002. *Anchorage Daily News* EPI3889

332 Mullen, Theo. "A Use For Biometrics?" *techweb.com*, Sept. 21, 2000. EPI2603

ID and the Bad Guys

My brother Mark Begich while serving on the Anchorage Assembly, our local government, proposed with others the use of cameras for traffic violators in school zones. This issue struck many of us as "Big Brother" and little brother Mark heard from the public with both support and strong opposition. The issue was taken to court in Alaska where the use of these systems was defeated at the time. Other communities in other states with less privacy protections have continued to advance these systems with mixed reviews. The trend is that these systems are making it into the mainstream and are surfacing in several communities. They are usually promoted as either revenue generators or security features for communities.

"Using City Link's closed-circuit cameras and electronic tags to book speeding drivers was a reasonable use of the cutting-edge technology, according to a random survey of potential users. But the developer, Transurban City Link, has already ruled out turning its cameras and toll gates into law-enforcement tools when the road network opens later next year. Sixty-one per cent of people surveyed last month, as part of a continuing study of community perceptions towards the $1.8 billion private road network, said it was reasonable to use the military tracking technology to fine law-breakers."333 This shift in public opinion is manipulated as people pushing the technologies learn to spin their story into publicly accepted norms. Yet even they have problems they might like to hide. "City Link's billing system is embroiled in controversy after revelations that an e-tag customer was charged $1645 because Transurban, the private developer of the tollway, wrongly deducted money from her bank account – 329 times. Stung by criticism over its inability to explain what is wrong with the City Link technology, Transurban yesterday conceded that three other customers had been incorrectly billed. But it maintained that the problems were isolated incidents."334

Other previously military only systems are also making their way forward. Voice information is also being considered for

333 McKay, Sandra. "City Link Tracking Speedsters Backed." *The Age*, Jan. 12, 1998. EPI1956

334 Das, Sushi. "The Big E-Tag Raises An Outcry In Australia." *The Age*, July 7, 1999. EPI1957

wider use as has been indicated before. "The objective of this effort is to provide a biometric identification capability using voice verification in a dedicated commuter lane, which allows registered entrants to cross the United States – Mexico border without normal inspection. This system, funded by the Immigration and Naturalization Service (INS), is being developed by a joint Air Force Research Lab (AFRL)–New York State Technology Enterprise Corporation (NYSTEC) team. A driver enrolled in the system is issued a hand-held unit. When entering the dedicated commuter lane, the driver speaks into the unit, which then transmits the voice sample via an infrared link to a roadside receiver. The voice sample is then forwarded to voice verification software developed by the Air Force Research Laboratory, which compares the voice sample to samples recorded when the driver registered to use the system and verifies the identity of the driver." 335 Voice is as unique as your fingerprint and can be used to isolate a phone call out of billions, like picking the right grain of sand on the beach of humanity.

Many of the revelations about the internal security apparatus in the United States were causing problems for the United States before September 11th. The FBI, NSA and CIA were all under fire from several quarters until that fateful event afterwhich most voices were silenced. "A year after two teams of experts concluded the National Security Agency was suffering profound operational and organizational problems, the director of the Ft. Meade, MD-based signals intelligence organization said last week he is beginning to see the initial benefits of a sweeping transformation effort aimed at changing the agency's culture, improving its technical capabilities and repairing its relationship with key stakeholders."336 Now three years later, these agencies have been given more authority, increased budgets and even less accountability intesifying the dangerous slide into the "new world order" – an Orwellian scenario most of us hoped could be avoided.

---

335 Justice Technology Information Network (JUSTNET). Project Status Report: In-Vehicle Voice Verification System. June 30, 2000. http://www.nlectc.org/techproj/ EPI2946

336 Lardner, Richard. "NSA Chief Pushes Ahead With Overhaul Of Agency's Culture, Operations." *Inside Defense,* Oct. 16, 2000. http://cryptome.org/nsa-reorg-id.htm EPI2759

The terror attacks did happen. Their impact on us all will be with us for the remainder of our lives. What were the terrorists after? Was it inflicting fear, insecurity and unrest into the economic and political systems of the West? Was it to destroy the platform of values that have led to the formation of the world's greatest democratic states?

If freedom is destroyed, if privacy is crushed and individual privacy traded for security, which is not really secure, at all, who wins? If we lose our values in a world of fear, hate and mistrust then we have lost the most important race of all. We have lost the essence of liberty and freedom which is the human race.

Locate Anything Anywhere
Novel Uses

There are a variety of uses for these new systems, which sound good on first examination by some and strike others quite differently. Tracking even cash flows in a much different way is expected to be possible. "Hitachi has developed a chip that could be woven into paper money to help identify counterfeits and could also have wide ramifications for identification and surveillance technologies. For example, chips could be implanted into all paper money and be connected wirelessly to the Internet so that authorities would be able to monitor the movement of all cash."337 Imagine tracing every dollar that trades hands and being able to locate it exactly anywhere on the planet. Readers of this information could count your cash as you pass through public places or calculate the amount of cash hidden under your mattress. Is this a good thing? It depends on your perspective and how the information might be used. Eventually all financial transactions, even cash, will be tied to the international system of transactions. All cash, credit and bank holdings could then be monitored in person-specific-ways allowing control of all commerce. Is this a good thing?

Business thinks these are great things for trade and marketing. Know the customer takes on all new meaning when so much can be ascertained about people based on their consumer activities, among other things, now traced by corporations and

337 *CNET News.com Staff.* "Hitachi in the money with tiny chip?" July 3, 2001. *http://news.cnet.com* EPI3570

government. "Wireless systems capable of tracking vehicles and people all over the planet are leaving businesses aglow with new possibilities, and some privacy advocates deeply concerned. These technologies have become one of the fastest-growing areas of the wireless communications industry. The market for location-based services is estimated at nearly $600 million and is forecast to approach $5 billion within three years..."338 Welcome to the wireless world and some of its more sinister applications. The balancing act is important here not just for the integration of these technologies but also their honest use. These systems need to be regulated against abuse after significant public discussion. Moreover, because these systems are subject to significant abuse, safeguards should be put in place and serious criminal penalties should be dished out to those who abuse these systems.

What do you have to Hide?

Politicians moved quickly to sack the latest bureaucratic tax scheme. "Michigan lawmakers may move to yank state funding for a controversial study into using satellites to tax drivers for every mile they travel. State Senator Bill Bullard Jr., chairman of the Transportation Committee, wants to revoke the state's $20,000 commitment to a $700,000 study of an odometer tax, which would have the effect of turning all roads into toll roads by tracking travel through global positioning systems." 339

Fines, taxes and supposed public safety are some of the many rationales being used to justify these systems. Even in liberal San Francisco these systems are gaining acceptance. "When a San Francisco-area driver zips through a FasTrak lane, a computer takes notice, documenting the information in a database from which it is possible for law enforcement officials or even lawyers to retrieve the data for an indefinite period of time. Automated toll lanes are becoming more and more available, prompting privacy advocates to question if new innovations in technology are making tracking people's movements all too easy. The ability to track people wherever they are is becoming greater.

---

338 Romero, Simon. *(New York Times* Service). "As Wireless Tracking is Born, Does Privacy Die?" *International Herald Tribune,* March 5, 2001. EPI3150

339 Kurth, Joel. "Odometer tax proposal likely to stall." *Detroit News,* March 9, 2001. EPI3220

Major automobile manufacturers are beginning to install Global Positioning Systems in more models coming off the assembly line, and Federal officials decreed that wireless device companies would be required to make their products so that any cellular phone call can be traced within a couple hundred feet so help can arrive quickly if 911 is called. However, some privacy advocates wonder if the intention to help is truly the primary reason for requiring such capabilities. California state law bars government institutions from making personal information available unless a court order is awarded, in which case the subject is to be notified first. The information that is logged when a FasTrak user cruises through the toll lane is specifically for billing purposes; however, the information does appear to serve other purposes. For instance, a car involved in a hit and run incident on a bridge in Vallejo, Calif., was identified thanks to FasTrak data, and detectives in New York reportedly scan the information regularly in order to track the movements of suspected criminals. Currently, over 100,000 Bay area drivers use the FasTrak toll service. (http://www.sfgate.com/)."340 Remember these things are all for your personal safety...maybe a little self-responsibility would be a better alternative to the open intrusion of government.

"Technology, which allows wireless companies to pinpoint the location of cellphone users in order to help them locate the nearest cash machine, gas station, or police station, is being tested by the California Highway Patrol in an attempt to help 911 callers. By October 2001, all wireless service providers must have the capability to find out their users' locations, according to a requirement from the Federal Communications Commission. This mandate could mean police departments will have access to the technology to pinpoint distressed callers that cannot give their locations. However, the technology has the potential to invade users' privacy and safety by giving wireless companies the ability to report their exact locations not only to the police, but to retailers as well. Under current laws, law enforcement officers are allowed to listen in on calls of potential criminals and obtain location details relevant to any case. Alan Davidson, staff counsel at the Center for Democracy and Technology and an opponent of such technology, believes it is

340 Wallack, Todd. *(San Francisco Chronicle).* "They Know Where You've Been." Feb. 12, 2001. *Law Enforcement & Corrections Technology News Summary,* Feb. 15, 2001. EPI3053

invasive and like an 'Orwellian nightmare,' depending on how the technology is used." 341

We want to emphasize that these systems are two edged in that they can provide advances which are useful and important. The balance is up to each of us to first find in ourselves and then express loudly in a vigorous public discussion of these technologies and their potential uses. "The Mercedes S-Class and Lexus LS 430 offer adaptive cruise control, which can help cars avoid collisions and navigate properly. Such systems would protect lives, shielding passengers with an electric cocoon of safety. Mercedes' cruise control allows the car to stay behind another vehicle at a set distance. The Lexus system has a laser beam that works to accelerate, slow, or brake to stay with the pace of traffic. These systems take away the need to reset cruise control. The complex technology makes driving more relaxing, says Michael Schamberger, president of Automotive Distance Control Systems GmBh. Cameras can offer drivers a 360-degree view so that blind spots can be located. If steering and braking is controlled through technology, the system could help keep a car on course. The 2002 Ford Explorer offers a rollover safety curtain that deploys a curtain before the car rolls, while Global Positioning Satellite systems can pinpoint a car's location, ending lost highways. Law enforcement may eventually use satellite traffic data to track suspects of crime and speeders, if privacy issues can be settled. It will, however, take greater acceptance of technology to lead to satellite-controlled traffic." 342

In support of increased corporate and worldwide monitoring the United States lowered the security bar to let others gain from GPS technology when the White House announced that, "Today, I am pleased to announce that the United States will stop the intentional degradation of the Global Positioning System (GPS) signals available to the public beginning at midnight tonight. We call this degradation feature Selective Availability (SA). This will mean that civilian users of GPS will be able to

341 Kirby, Carrie. *(San Francisco Chronicle)*. "New Technology Can Pinpoint Cell-Phone Users' Locations." Oct. 23, 2000. *Law Enforcement & Corrections Technology News Summary*, Oct. 26, 2000. EPI2924

342 Ulrich, Lawrence. *(Detroit Free Press)*. "Adaptive Cruise Control Offers Glimpse Into Safer Future for Cars." Oct. 26, 2000. *Law Enforcement & Corrections Technology News Summary*, Nov. 9, 2000. EPI2922

pinpoint locations up to ten times more accurately than they do now."[343]

"Michael Fattouche, president and CEO of Cell-Loc Inc., has received a patent for a type of wireless technology that can be used to indicate the location of cell phone users who dial 911. With the millions of US and Canadian mobile phone company clients who make these calls, demand for the service is likely to be especially heavy. In fact, mobile phone carriers in the United States will be required to implement this feature by October 2001. But while the initial purpose of these devices is for 911 phone call emergencies, Fattouche hopes to market them in several other fields, including law enforcement. According to Fattouche, Cell-Loc has the ability to use its wireless technology to track the movement of stolen goods, criminals, or any other device or person whose movement must be monitored. Fattouche's plan is to establish relationships with wireless carriers such as AT&T in which the carriers will have free access to using the devices to track 911 calls, in exchange for allowing Cell-Loc to use their transmission towers for signal detection. Cell-Loc has already formed an agreement with a Brazilian firm to provide the service for the insurance and banking industry, and Fattouche says there is much more potential for the systems to be used by law enforcement officials in Central and South America. Cell-Loc is also targeting Alberta, Canada to run a trial program to determine in which locations and fields the technology will be most effective."[344] Again the multinational companies look toward more repressive societies as the place to sell their technologies. This commercial activity, while beneficial to corporate interests, fails to respect human interests. What is not tolerated in the countries where these technologies first developed is explored with government subsidies to abuse other innocent people around the world. Welcome to the New World Order.

343 The White House, Office of the Press Secretary. "Statement By The President Regarding The United States Decision To Stop Degrading Global Positioning Accuracy." May 1, 2000. EPI2617

344 *Canadian Business.* "Be Careful How You Use Your Cell Phone." *Law Enforcement & Corrections Technology News Summary,* March 16, 2000. EPI2025

Chapter 7

The Future of Technology

Afterword

Often we are asked what a person can do and our answer remains the same – get involved. Politics and political change have often been the subject of this writer and we have published a number of ideas which are useful in creating change. We have written some essays on these subjects which can be accessed for free on the Internet at our website www.earthpulse.com. At that site are a series of articles under the index key "Empowerment". These essays may be passed on to others as long as they are not used commercially. Read them. If useful, pass them on and let us know what you think.

In these pages we have attempted to disclose a number of technologies that offer in some cases great promise while in others, significant challenges for us all, no matter where we reside on the planet.

Earthpulse Press has, over the years, been in the forefront of this debate by compiling material and making it available to the public in order to encourage thinking and discussion. We are hard on the technologies not because we oppose them all, we do not. Our interest is an open discussion that can lead to, and assure, proper use of technology.

The world will always be a place where humans create the greatest outcomes and hold the greatest destructive potentials. Over time our ability to bring life or take it has increased to levels never contemplated before. Some of the new threats include terrorism, revolution, economic disruption and drug trafficking, which are often the targets of the new militarization. Ideology no longer is relevant to many of the outcomes of government as special interests solidify their control of politics creating fragmented national policies devoid of many of our democratic republic's basic beliefs. Economic policy – the international policy of greed – is what drives much of what is happening in the world without consideration of the impacts. It will be people who make the difference in these technologies – the activists of the 21st century.

There are wonderful people involved with many of the companies and organizations criticized in these pages and we are not making an indictment of them. We are calling on people of good will to keep in front of each of us the higher values of humanity. To seek peace is still a noble cause even in the climate of war we are living through today. Perhaps for Americans this will remind us of what so many others face in a very insecure world everyday. The decisions of this generation will determine the direction of liberty and freedom, peace or war and a living or dead planet.

The United States, at this moment in history, is the most powerful country on Earth. We have the power to effect natural planetary regulatory systems in the sea, air, on land and even in space. We have gained the power to manipulate living systems, the environment, and machines like no civilization before us. The challenges are not distant from us but all around us now. What this generation of living souls decides will determine whether we destroy the world and civil society, create a new world order reflective of corrupt corporate values or move to a higher set of human values. The choice is ours.

The subtitle of this book is *The Betrayal of Science, Society and the Soul.* The title was chosen because this is what we believe has happened. I think of the stories of my personal interactions along life's journey and am encouraged in knowing that a few people can still make a difference. We have been in the fight for what we believe is true freedom – the unleashing of human potential into a direction of positive change. Our hope is that the words on these pages encourage others to rise to the challenge and join with us.

Every great thing which has ever happened on the planet started with a single soul or a small group of thinkers. We each hold incredible creative potential and the ability to impact the world around us in significant ways. In the nine years that have passed since we started discussing many of these ideas a lot has changed, and we are even more convinced we are on the right path. Change begins with each of us stepping into the issue we believe important. Each of us has issues worth pursuing and we encourage all to so engage.

All good things happen when we each begin to act on what is right and true. Today is a good day to begin.

Appendix A

Definitions and Descriptions of New Technology Concepts

"***Acoustic Beam***. High power, very low frequency beam emitted from weaponry under development. Envisioned to be a piston-driven or detonation-driven pulser which forces compressed air into tubes to generate a low frequency wave.

Acoustic Bullets. High power, very low frequency waves emitted from one to two meter antenna dishes. Results in blunt object trauma from waves generated in front of the target. Effects range from discomfort to death. A Russian device that can propel a 10-hertz sonic bullet the size of a baseball hundreds of yards is thought to exist. Proposed fixed site defense. Also known as sonic bullets.

Acoustic, Deference Tones. Devices which can project a voice or other sound to a particular location. The resulting sound can only be heard at that location.

Acoustic, Infrasound. Very low-frequency sound which can travel long distances and easily penetrate most buildings and vehicles. Transmission of long wavelength sound creates biophysical effects; nausea, loss of bowels, disorientation, vomiting, potential internal organ damage or death may occur. Superior to ultrasound because it is 'in band' meaning that it does not lose its properties when it changes mediums such as from air to tissue. By 1972 an infrasound generator had been built in France which generated waves at 7 hertz. When activated it made people in range sick for hours.

Acoustic & Optical, Photic Driver. A crowd control device developed by a British company prior to 1973 which uses ultrasound and flashing infrared lights which penetrate closed human eyelids. Potential for epileptic fits because of the stroboscopic flashing effect. May have been employed by South African Police during interrogations.

Acoustic & Optical, Psycho-Correction. A technology invented by a Russian scientist that involves influencing subjects visually or aurally with embedded subliminal messages.

Acoustic & Optical, Stun Grenade. A non-lethal grenade, XM84, in development to be used by Army military police.

Baton, Biotechnical-Injector. A baton with an automatic self-injecting syringe for administering the antidote to nerve gas built into it's tip and filled with calmatives or other biotechnical agents.

Baton, Electrical. Standard dimension baton which delivers an electric charge of low voltage, powered by standard flash-light cells. Also known as a stun baton or shock baton.

Baton, Riot Control Agent. 12-36" plastic baton which is able to project riot control agents.

Baton, Straight, Flashlight-Riot Control Agent. Shock resistance polyethylene flashlight. Besides providing a light source, this flashlight can be used as a baton and to project a riot-control agent.

Biotechnical, Calmatives. Biotechnical agents which are sedatives or sleep-inducing drugs; includes alfentinil, fentanyls, ketamine and BZ. Several of them make ideal choices for this application when mixed with dimethyl sulfoxide (DMSO), which promotes absorption through skin to quickly sedate persons contacted. DMSO introduces the calmative agent into the bloodstream by increasing the epidermal absorption rate by about 1,000 percent. The explosion of a flash-bang (sometimes called a diversionary device) represents one method of dispersing DMSO and a calmative agent. Calmatives were reportedly used by the Soviets against the Mujahideen in Afganistan. Also known as sleep agents.

Biotechnical, Genetic Alteration. The act of changing genetic code to create a desired less-than-lethal but long-term disablement effect, perhaps for generations, thereby creating a societal burden.

Biotechnical, Neuro-Implant. Computer implants into the brain which allow for behavior modification and control. Current research is experimental in nature and focuses on lab animals such as mice.

Biotechnical, Maladorous Agents. Foul-smelling gases and sprays such as hydrogen sulphide (H2S) or a compound known as NaS8 which is used in making plastics. Could be delivered by a grenade. Past work on 'cultural specific' agents has also been undertaken.

Biotechnical, Wetware. Advanced technology devices which are surgically implanted into the body rather than worn. These devices can be used to enhance memory and the human senses, modify behavior or to locate allied troops. Pacemakers represent an early form of wetware. New concept developed in this document.

Electrical, Projector. An advanced version of the standoff stun gun, where no wires are required. The charges are delivered through pre-ionized air channels or by charging a low energy projectile which releases the charge at impact. Another approach is to launch a low energy projectile that releases the electrical charge at impact by compressing a piezoelectric element.

Electrical, Water Stream. A mobile unit projects a water stream charged with high voltage, low amperage. Another method cites 2 water jets, 1 negatively charged and 1 positively charged, which meet to close the circuit.

Electromagnetic, Engine Kill. The use of high-powered microwaves to kill the electrical system of an engine.

Electromagnetic, High Power Microwave (HPM), Weapons. Energy generated by a conventional electromagnetic apparatus, such as a radar transmitter, or released from a conventional explosion converted into a radio-frequency weapon which causes the disruption of electronic systems. Usually an ultra-wide band source focus due to target vulnerability considerations. HPMs can also cause human unconsciousness without permanent maiming by upsetting the neural pathways in the brain and/or death.

Electromagnetic, Interference (EMI). Flight control systems of military aircraft are sensitive to electromagnetic interference (EMI). It is suspected that several crashes of Army

UH-60 Black Hawk helicopters may have resulted when they flew too near large microwave transmitters.

Electromagnetic, Radio Frequency (RF), Weapons. A class of weapons which transmit short, high-powered pulses of electromagnetic radiation over significant ranges.

Hologram, Death. Hologram used to scare a target individual to death. Example, a drug lord with a weak heart sees the ghost of his dead rival appearing at his bedside and dies of fright.

Obscurant, Smoke-Colored. Colored smoke concentrations produce greater initial psychological and panic effect than white smoke. Caucasians are said to have a greater repugnance to brilliant green smoke, which is associated with disagreeable personal experiences such as seasickness, bile and vomit. Negroids and Latins are declared to be most adversely affected by brilliant red. Rioters confronted with a strong concentration of colored smoke feel, instinctively, that they are being marked, or stained, and thus they lose anonymity.

Optical, Cobra. Prototype of the AN/PLQ-5 Laser Countermeasures System. A 30-pound hand-held laser weapon used to damage enemy sensors and human eyes. Because this device may operate on three different wave lengths it may be impossible to be currently defended against.

Projectile, Gas Vortex. If a gas vortex, a highly stable phenomena, was projected at some velocity, the difference in pressure on the leading and trailing edges would produce an impact. Potential use in crowd and riot control situations.

Theoretical, Twenty-First Century Politico-Military Force Matrix. Nonlethal technology, when coupled with traditional forms of lethal weaponry, allow for the application of short-term incapacitation, long-term incapacitation, and deadly force against the physical and mental/perceptual attributes of human targets and the hardware and software attributes of machine targets. This advanced form of politico-military force application can be expressed in a matrix." 345

---

345 Bunker et al. *Non-Lethal Weapons: Terms and References.* INSS Occasional Paper 15, USAF Institute for National Security Studies, USAF Academy, Colorado. July 1997. EPI3349

Resource Guide

Earthpulse USA
P. O. Box 201393
Anchorage, Alaska 99520 USA

24 Hours a Day
VISA or Master Card Accepted
Voice Mail Ordering: 1-907-249-9111
http://www.earthpulse.com

A FREE CATALOG of all of our products and books is available on request.

1. ***Bringing the War Home,*** by William Thomas is a controversial book which explores and challenges the ideas surrounding the events in the Gulf War. Through careful research, and a new perspective, the author describes the problems leading to the conflict and the startling results. The U.S. government's cover-up and military personnel's exposure to biological weapons is detailed in the most incredible exposé ever written on the subject. But it doesn't stop there – in the 448 pages of this book a cure for some of the diseases is detailed. The book is $22.95 shipped airmail in the U.S. or $27.95 internationally.

2. ***Scorched Earth: The Military's Assault on the Environment,*** by William Thomas is a detailed account of how the military has exposed Americans and people around the world to toxic risks they never disclosed. Every page contains well-footnoted evidence of how our lives have been negatively affected by the lack of concern for the impact of military technology. The book is $19.95 Air Mail in the U.S. or $21.95 Air Mail internationally.

3. ***Earthpulse Flashpoints*** is a Microbook series edited by Dr. Nick Begich. Microbooks cover four major areas: government, frontier health sciences, earth science, and new technologies. The goal of the publication is to get hard-to-find information into the hands of individuals on their road to self empowerment and self discovery. Nine issues published 48-64 pages each. $6.95 in the U.S. and $9.95 internationally.

4. ***Angels Don't Play this HAARP: Advances in Tesla Technology*** is a book about non-lethal weapons, mind control, weather warfare and the government's plan to control the environment or maybe even destroy it in the name of national defense. The book is $18.95 Air Mail in the U.S. or $23.95 internationally.

5 . ***Angles Don't Play This HAARP – THE VIDEO.*** This is a video lecture by Dr. Nick Begich produced by L. L. Productions of Seattle, Washington. Approximate running time 1 hour 45 minutes. 33.00 in the U.S. or $39.00 international.

6. ***Earth Rising – The Revolution: Toward a Thousand Years of Peace,*** by Dr. Nick Begich and James Roderick. This book is a book about new technology and the impacts of new technology on humanity. The book is footnoted with over 650 source references spanning fifty years of innovations. The book includes advances in the Revolution in Military Affairs, mind control and manipulation of human health, non-lethal weapons, privacy erosion and numerous other areas where technology is impacting mankind. The conclusion of the book contains an overview and series of actions which could be initiated which would return us to a more civil and open society. The book is $23.00 Air Mail in the U.S. or $29.00 internationally.

7. ***Holes in Heaven – THE VIDEO.*** This documentary film narrated by Martin Sheen explains both sides of the debate surrounding the HAARP issue and includes the military, scientists and those opposed to the technology. This video is $33.00 Air Mail in the U.S. or $37.00 internationally.

8. ***Weapons of the New World Order – THE VIDEO.*** This in-studio video is a two hour and forty minute discussion of new weapons technology from a Christian perspective. The topics include the latest information on HAARP, non-lethal weapons, weather modification, mind control and other controversial issues. The video is $28.00 Air Mail in the U.S. or $31.00 internationally.

11. ***Earth Rising II: The Betrayal of Science, Society and the Soul,*** by Dr. Nick Begich and James Roderick. This book is a book about underwater sonar, cell phones, energy weapons, implant technology, privacy and other emerging technologies. The book is footnoted with over 300 source references spanning fifty years of innovations. The conclusion of the book contains an overview and series of actions which could be initiated which would return us to a more civil and open society. The book is $23.00 Air Mail in the U.S. or $29.00 internationally.

New Sound of the Soundwave™!

COMING SOON!

The most advanced sound transfer technology available anywhere in the world is currently being beta-tested in Europe for introduction to the United States. This new technology will allow for the transfer of sound directly through the body by-passing the normal hearing mechanism. For more information on this technology contact Earthpulse USA at the above address.

This technology has been developed with superior technology created in Europe in 2001-2002. The technology far surpasses the performance of earlier sound devices in several applications by integrating modern circuit designs with 21st century engineering. The technology delivers sound energy through a biologically compatible signal. This technology will be made available in late 2002 for accelerated learning applications, body system balancing and trials in hearing enhancement applications.

Authors James Roderick and Dr. Nick Begich
Eagle River, Alaska